The How To Feel Good Handbook

By

Elayne J. Kahn, Ph.D.

and

Gael McCarthy

VECTOR PRESS

New York City

Printed in the United States

All Rights Reserved

Vector Marketing Inc.

New York, New York

© Copyright 1984 VECTOR MARKETING, INC.

ISBN 0-917259-01-7

The poem "No" by Jose Luis Hidalgo is from "Grief" by Stephan Berg. © 1973 by
Stephan Berg. Reprinted by permission of Viking Penguin Inc.

FOREWORD

Of course, life has its ups and downs, but we are lucky to be living in a time when, thanks to medical and psychological know-how, we can influence the ways in which outside circumstances affect us. We can learn how to make the ups last longer and occur more often and how to make the downs less frequent and less intense. In short, The How To Feel Good Handbook will help you do just what it says—help you feel good.

CONTENTS

CHAPTER I

HOW TO FEEL GOOD BY LIKING YOURSELF

If you are feeling okay but would like to feel better, if you are feeling not-so-okay and would like to feel good, if you are feeling terrible and can't remember what it's like to feel good—it has been so long—this book has been written for you.

In it, you will find a few questions, a lot of suggestions and a variety of answers, some of which will be "right" for you. Ultimately, you will be your own scorekeeper in that regard, but to get as many treasures as you can—to derive as much good as possible for yourself from this handbook, you will have to be honest with yourself.

The first and foremost person in your life is you. Feeling good about life, generally, begins with feeling good about yourself, specifically. If you do not like yourself, you will not even *let* yourself feel good.

DO YOU LIKE YOURSELF?

Hardly anyone who answers that question thoughtfully will be able to say, "Yes. I like myself totally, just the way I am is fine with me." Most people have many qualities they like in themselves and some that they would like to correct or adjust to greater or lesser degrees. On a scale of 1 to 10, where would you place your liking for yourself—at 3? 5? 8?

Mark it on this line:

I like myself 1   5   10

If we asked you to make a list of your "good" and "not-so-good" points, what would you write? Here are the lists made by two "regular" people:

Amanda is a normal, likeable person. She isn't perfect, but all in all is finding life a good experience, despite—perhaps even because of—her mixed bag of traits. We asked her to make up an inventory of her traits and this is how she described herself:

AMANDA, 27, single

GOOD POINTS	NOT-SO-GOOD POINTS
Witty	I sometimes try too hard to be clever
Generous	
Think for myself	Resent it when people aren't generous to me as well
Intelligent	
Trustworthy	Impatience with the not-too-bright
Use my talents	
Know my own feelings	Cheat on my income tax
	Coast on my abilities—could improve
Sensitive to feelings of others	
Loyal friend	Let my feelings show, when I shouldn't

8

Well read	Play "shrink" too often
Good at budgeting money	Fickle about men
Good sense of color, style	Don't throw out newspapers, magazines
Energetic	Can be too bargain-conscious
Like being with people	Worry too much about clothes
Nice smile	Not efficient about planning time use
	Should spend more time alone, thinking
	Too-curly hair

Mike is a normal, likeable person, too. He isn't perfect either, but like all of us is an amalgam of good and not-so-good qualities. His self-description follows:

MIKE, 28, single

GOOD POINTS	NOT-SO-GOOD POINTS
Friendly	Short
Intelligent	Colorblind
Good at improvising solutions	Don't plan ahead
Imaginative	Daydream too much
Well-informed about work	Have been called nosy
Laid back	Often late for work, appointments
Tuned-in to people	Forget to tune out
Women like me	Get involved with too many women

9

GOOD POINTS	NOT-SO-GOOD POINTS
Get things done quickly	Sometimes go too fast with projects
Informative	Don't always keep secrets
Diplomatic	Don't believe what people say at times
Cheery	
Know how to flatter	Want to be liked too much
Funny	Am not always sincere

Amanda's list shows her to be more self-accepting and matter-of-fact than Mike. His descriptions show he is aware of some faults—and their ramifications—but don't indicate a strong intent on change, just a tendency to scold himself about them. Surprisingly, Amanda, who is often called beautiful, mentioned only a "nice smile" as a physical asset under her Good Points column and her too-curly hair as a Not-So-Good point. Both descriptions are at the bottom of the list, however, probably indicating that her physical appearance is not of major importance to her. She has good points that balance out her less-than-ideal traits: She says she can be a loyal friend, however fickle she can be with men. She's proud of her wit but has come to realize that it can be overdone and is proud of her intelligence but not proud of her impatience with those who seem less bright than she. Amanda is fairly aware of her strengths and seems to be working on her weaknesses with optimism. She gives herself an 8, on a rating scale of 1 to 10.

Mike's list of traits describe a person who is seeking approval from others but who doesn't approve of himself enough. He said that initially, writing out this inventory seemed a "fun thing" to do. It wasn't till much later that he began to really think of what it meant to him. At the time, he gave himself a 7 rating on a scale of 1 to 10. The next day, he told us, he had revised it to a 5. Looking over his list made him realize he had some work to do if he were going to feel as good as he'd like to feel. Jokingly, he said that he was buying elevated shoes immediately. Then he seriously said he'd start planning ahead more, "even if it does cut into my chances to show how good I am at improvising." Mike seemed genuinely surprised at how much insight into himself this simple exercise had given him.

Most of us say we are too busy (and mean we are a little afraid) to take a good look at ourselves. But, when we do, we find there is a great deal worth knowing. (And why shouldn't you know as much or more about yourself than do the people who associate with you?) You can't like yourself until you know yourself, after all. Amanda had a fairly good amount of self-knowledge and, despite her less-than perfect status, liked herself quite a lot. Mike learned of traits he never realized he had and decided to work on his self-portrait—not because people would like him more if he did, but because he would like himself more. Now make your own list of good points and not-so-good points. Be specific and write down everything you can think of. Then pick out the not-so-good point you're going to start working on now.

HOW TO LIKE YOURSELF MORE

First, liking yourself means acknowledging who and what you are and, following a clear-eyed assessment of

11

your good and not-so-good points, deciding what to change and what to keep. If you can do this without nagging yourself, without concentrating on all that's wrong with you and negating all that's positive about you, you will have an enjoyable time of it. The people you like in your life are not perfect and nobody— including you—should expect to be perfect, either. Take a look at the things about yourself you really *WANT* to change. Not the things you think you *OUGHT* to change. If you are convinced that you *CAN* change them and would be happier if you changed them, make a plan to do so—and then *START*. But set reasonable goals: You *can't* stop being short. You *can* stop wasting energy hating the fact that you're short. You *can't* stop—overnight—being overweight. You *can* stop old behaviors that make being overweight inevitable. You *can't* stop being in need of money just by *wishing* you weren't. You *can* start budgeting and draw up a financial management plan to take effect today.

Probably the best way to feel good about yourself is—to quote a familiar prayer—work to "accept with serenity the things that cannot be changed, to have the courage to change the things which should be changed, and the wisdom to know the difference."

When you don't like yourself it is often because you compare yourself to others and you judge yourself to be inferior. Run down the lists of qualities possessed by those you admire, whether you're considering a neighbor or Jane Fonda or an astronaut. Then do a mental review of your own traits. Ask yourself: "Of them all, whose personal traits would I trade for my own—on a 100 percent basis? You will undoubtedly find that no one person possesses all the positive qualities you admire.

12

We're pretty sure that, when you've gotten right down to it, the answer you'll come up with is: "I'll keep my own." You'd rather be you. You see, you do like yourself! And with good reason. You have special characteristics that no one else has. It's good to be you. The real you. Faults and all.

Okay, you'd rather be you. You can accept the less-than-perfect aspects of yourself. Does that mean the package is complete, no alterations necessary? A finished product? It could—if you want it to, if you're going to feel good that way. But acceptance need not preclude alterations. In fact, once you become familiar with your own personal architecture, you become more capable of changing it to suit your desires.

HOW TO LOOK FORWARD TO CHANGE

Given what you know of yourself, and of what you've come to know of life, if you could manage it, there might be a few things you'd like to accomplish for the sheer fun of it.

For example, complete the following sentences:
"I've always wanted to travel to _____"
"I've always wanted to be _____"
"I've always wanted to do _____"
"I've always wanted to learn to _____"
"If there were three people I could get to know really well in this town, they would be _____"
"Someday, just for the heck of it, I'd like to ____"

If you've wanted to circle the globe, be several pounds thinner, quit smoking, learn to ride horseback, speak fluent French, hang-glide or hob-nob with tennis champions, maybe you should examine the possibilities. Since so many of these projects sound like fun, doesn't it make you wonder: If you've really "always wanted to" do them, then why haven't you?

Perhaps you haven't done some of these things because they are just pleasant fantasies and not wishes.

Perhaps you don't think you deserve to feel that good.

Perhaps you haven't done them because you're afraid even to try—you might *SUCCEED*—and make your life extremely—perhaps frighteningly—different from the way it has always been. ("How," asks a small voice somewhere inside you, "how would I handle it, if things changed too much? Would the people I'm close to now not like it (or me) if I became too different (from them or from who I am now)?

Perhaps you're afraid you might *FAIL*. ("What if I *really try*—and find out I *can't*?")

Change. It is probably the scariest word known to man. Its possibility alone triggers such reactions as: "Why risk the known for the unknown? We know what we have—things might get worse." Another version of this is, "The world is so uncertain anyway, it's good to have things you can rely on." (That's okay, so far as it goes—if the things you can rely on are good things and not merely familiar things.)

Sometimes change is for the best and worth the risk. It can even be something to look forward to, rather than to dread.

Perhaps the best thing about making a decision to change some aspect of yourself is realizing that you can be in control. Suppose that you establish a reasonable goal that can be accomplished and will benefit you (and not hurt others) and then work to make it happen. You are making something happen *for* you, rather than merely having life happen *to* you. Determining what you want to change and planning the best way to go about effecting that change are the first steps. Methodically carrying out that plan is the next one, and taking action results in a feeling of control and confidence.

A dieter tells a friend: "I kept to my calorie limit all morning. I'm sure I can do it again at lunchtime."

A shy fellow who wants to be more outgoing has resolved to start by saying hello to people he knows at work, even though he's never really carried on conversations with them.

"I blushed," he recalls, "when I told the pretty receptionist good morning, and I stuttered saying hello to the boss, but I smiled, too—that's more than I ever dared to do before—and, of course, he smiled back!"

These two changelings are goal-setters who are reinforcing their good work, saluting their accomplishments. They are not waiting helplessly for some fairy godmother to transform them effortlessly into ideal beings. Instead, they are acknowledging the need to change within themselves because they *want* something better. They like themselves enough to try. People who don't like themselves will sabotage their own efforts—pooh-pooh their first small moves—and stop moving altogether. (The all—right now—or nothing at all attitude is one of the most popular in the sabotage market. Oftener than not, when someone doesn't pursue the goal aimed for, this is the block that has been stumbled over.)

"A journey of a thousand miles begins with but a single step," noted the Chinese philosopher, Lao Tzu, in the 6th Century, B.C. The message still holds. If you

15

make your changes one step at a time and salute yourself at every step, you'll get where you want to be—and you'll enjoy both the process and the achievement.

Not all changes are earth-shattering, heart-clattering events. Rita, an executive secretary, made a change at the drop of a remark, by a man in an elevator. She was leaving work around 8:15 one evening, tired after three hours of overtime, and carrying her usual number of shopping bags (three) filled to the brim and straining at their straps. The bags were full of office work still to be done, Rita's own personal papers, some books she'd been carrying back and forth for months, intending to read them, maybe, if she got time. There were also two pairs of shoes destined for the shoemaker for the last three weeks. Her biceps were becoming impressive, after three or more years of lugging these bags around.

Certainly the bags had impressed the man on the elevator enough to prompt him to say, "You secretaries—honestly, you all look like well-dressed shopping bag ladies. What do you have in those bags? All your earthly possessions?"

Rita laughed and lauded his wit. And when she got home she sorted through those bags, put the office work into a manilla folder and vowed never to take another shopping bag on the job as long as she lived. She never wondered about it, never said "I should" or "I ought to" or asked, "What if . . ." She simply decided that it would be easy to do this and make her life easier to take care of things immediately rather than continually carry them around to "do eventually."

Sorting through the stuff in those bags she found dated junk, two theater passes, bills that needed

16

paying that moment and store coupons that could never be considered for the Smithsonian's archives. She rid herself of the rubbish and made use of the prizes those bags contained—and found her hands free for better things.

We are all like Rita, sometimes. We carry around heavy packages of set-aside emotions, hopes and guilts and avoid looking at them—afraid of what we'll find, carrying them out of habit. They must be worth something—they're ours, aren't they? We could choose, instead to lighten our burden, toss out the trash and enjoy the treasures. That's what change is really about.

Take a look at who you are and what you have done with your life so far. On a scale of 1 to 10—right now—how do you feel about yourself? Your accomplishments? On a scale of 1 to 10 where would you like to be able to rate yourself six months from now?

NOW		**IN SIX MONTHS**	
1	10	1	10

If, by getting a new job, vacationing in the Caribbean or paying your bills on time, you would be moved to rate your self-esteem at 8 or 9 instead of 3 or 4, wouldn't it be worth the effort?

Give yourself permission to feel better about yourself. Set up a plan, congratulate yourself each time you follow through on it and cheer yourself on—don't harangue yourself—when you fail. Be the kind and loving parent to yourself that you wish you had had when you were growing up (and let yourself grow more—and feel good about it).

Make room for the person you choose to be. Some of

the situations and attitudes you live with—and settle for—every day are like old hand-me-downs from family and friends, enemies and associates from the past. Give them up. You don't need hand-me-downs. You can have new things—custom-tailored to your present-day wishes and needs.

SUMMARY:

It's important to get to know yourself and to like yourself if you want to feel good about life. Once you feel good about you, you can allow yourself the privilege and freedom to change.

Change is scary. It means letting go of the old. It also is rewarding, offering new treasures for old burdens. And it means work. Habit and inertia are barriers to change. One is hard to shake, the other is self-promoting. You might fail, but if you try and find you enjoyed the process of working to make something happen to you, rather than merely waiting for it to happen to you, succeeding will be secondary to the knowledge that you can take charge and rearrange some aspects of your world to your liking. Take the risk—you'll learn a great deal and there's almost no way you can lose.

CHAPTER II

HOW TO FEEL GOOD BY LIKING OTHERS

(And Having Them Like You)

> "The only way to have a friend
> is to be one."—Ralph Waldo Emerson

Everybody needs to feel appreciated, liked, wanted, needed. We want to share our lives with others. As young Frankie put it in Carson McCullers' play, *The Member of the Wedding*, we yearn to feel part of a "we."

If feeling good starts with our liking ourselves, it proceeds with our liking others—and feeling that they like us. Others give us feedback, tell us about ourselves, themselves. They react to our views and behaviors and we to theirs. Others are our touchstones—they test our mettle, strike responsive chords in us, incite us to action, calm our fears. They can make life pleasant, annoying, fulfilling, uncomfortable, challenging. For all their bother, others are essential. We do not thrive in isolation booths.

That old query, "If a tree falls in a forest and there is no one to hear, does it fall?" comes to mind and raises a similar thought: Can a human being be fully human if there is no other human being around to share yourself with?

With the exception of monks, healthy people need to relate to people; need to like them and be liked back. If you find yourself disliking people more often than liking them, you'll do yourself a favor if you find out why. Generally, liking is reciprocal. (You've got to like you before someone else does and, to extend the same idea in another direction, hardly any of us like people who don't like us.)

Of course, nobody is going to be able to like everybody (or even *any*body) all the time. However—it *is* possible to like almost everybody some of the time. In fact, learning to like people is a lot like learning to like olives; it's an acquired taste.

But don't try faking your feelings—somehow people can sense pretense. Take time to master the art of accepting people—even those you are not naturally drawn to.

Is there someone you dislike so intensely that the tension you feel in that individual's presence is a problem? If so, it is time to take control of the situation. Here are some suggestions that work well—if you use them:

- Remember that if you don't *like* some people totally, it doesn't necessarily follow that you must *dislike* them totally. With minimal effort, you will almost always be able to find something likable about them. (Maybe they're nice to their mothers. Maybe (at least) they're nice to animals. There's bound to be something.)
- Concentrate on as many good points in such persons as you can possibly dredge up. A per-

sonality inventory (CHAPTER 1) might help.

- Find out how others feel about this person and try to learn why. Have they found good qualities that have escaped your notice? Have they found "good" qualities that you found galling?
- Ask yourself why one person elicits such different responses from different persons. Why do you feel so strongly negative about this individual when others are so fond of him?

EXAMINE YOUR MOTIVES

When you dislike someone intensely, the reasons for such dislike probably lie outside the person and within yourself. Try to express what it is about a person's qualities that you dislike. Be specific. Be honest. Take your time—be complete.

We often take a dislike to someone without knowing why. Explore what, how, and why you feel the way you do and you'll probably discover that a discomfort within yourself is at the root of such feelings. Don't be afraid of what you might find—the process will be helpful, as it was in the following cases.

Certainly it helped Milton.

"Harriet—I can't stand that awful, cackling laugh of Betty's. I don't want her around here any more and that's all there is to it." Milton was shouting, in a rage. He'd never seemed to mind Betty before and, after 20 years of friendship with Betty, her best friend from early childhood, Harriet was shocked to hear his words.

Milton and Harriet had been married for nearly six years when he suddenly expressed this violent dislike for Betty, a woman he had tolerated easily enough until her recent divorce. Since her marriage had dissolved, Betty was constantly visiting Harriet, recounting her romantic adventures in detail. Milton would overhear them giggling or laughing and he found himself resentful of his wife's listening to such stories.

Without acknowledging it—even to himself— Milton was upset because he feared that Harriet eventually would want to share in Betty's adventures. He also was angry at Harriet's willingness to spend so much time with Betty. He couldn't say so, but he was jealous of the attention his wife was giving her friend. She seemed more interested in Betty than in Milton, her own husband.

It was only after Milton confronted Harriet and allowed himself to express his feelings—and really look at the cause of his distress that the situation improved.

Once Milton understood the source of his anger and told Harriet, she could respond to him. She treated his feelings with sensitivity and scheduled her time with Betty so that they would intrude less on the time that she and Milton shared. She also explained her motives to him. Betty had been her good friend through the years and, at this difficult time in her chum's life, Harriet wanted to be a good friend in return. She told him that, for all her laughter, Betty was feeling frightened and alone. Harriet felt sorry for Betty.

She also said she loved Milton deeply, was glad to have him for her husband and was happy to be his wife.

Milton took in this message and was then able

to relax about Betty, whom he once more regarded as Harriet's friend—and not an enemy to his marriage. Fear had motivated his anger at Betty. Once he knew Betty did not threaten him (that his wife loved him) he was no longer afraid or angry.

Sometimes we mask our feelings cleverly. For example, we might tell ourselves—and others—that we dislike someone for their poor social behavior. But that's not the reason—it's just an excuse to vent it.

Alice's dislike of Maria was an example of this:

Although Alice, 53, was the office manager, she didn't get much respect from Maria, a shapely 20-year-old in the secretarial pool. Unlike the rest of the women, who would go to Alice with requests for office supplies or permission to leave work early, Maria resorted to her own devices to get what she wanted. Whenever Maria needed something, she'd leave her desk and wiggle her way into the boss's office.

Even through the closed door, Alice could hear hushed tones interspersed with giggles. It made her furious.

Alice did not realize that her anger at Maria had as much to do with her envy of Maria's youth and attractiveness as it had to do with the young woman's disdain for Alice's authority. Maria's bypassing of Alice made it clear to everyone (or so Alice thought) that the older woman was unable to do her job and control the office staff.

It was only when Alice started asking others how they felt about Maria that she learned Maria

23

was well-liked. They described her as helpful, a willing and efficient worker, responsible, independent, cheerful, dependable, playful and one who liked to please and be liked. They also said she "flirted" with both men and women because she craved their acceptance. It was, said one co-worker, "just Maria's way." Alice began to see that the problem was really hers—and it stemmed from envy and feeling insufficiently recognized by Maria as the authority in the office and therefore out of control as office manager.

Since she could neither make herself younger nor age Maria, Alice reasoned that she'd better let go of her resentment. She proved her managerial skills by making Maria's duties clear, but giving her lots of leeway in which to perform them. Ultimately, both women grew to work well together—not liking each other but short of dislike.

Learning what others thought about Maria prompted Alice to *question her own reactions* to Maria and opened her eyes to her attitude about aging and about exercising authority. By concentrating and capitalizing on Maria's good points, she saved the situation.

We can't always know what others feel about us or about others. But we *can* try to examine the reasons for our own feelings which, sometimes, are obvious to everyone but ourselves.

LOOK AT THE TOTAL PERSON

From where you sit, a person may appear to be an idiot, a skinflint, a boor. From where others are viewing him, however, he appears to be an okay guy with some rather endearing idiosyncracies. Why the distortion? George wondered, himself:

"Harry is the kind of fellow who was born grumpy, practices being grumpy at least 20 times a day and could be awarded the grump championship of the decade—maybe even the century—if it were offered. He is also a male chauvinist pig and I, a man, can say that. I hated going to his house, hated seeing him boss his wife, Thelma around, taking her for granted. It embarrassed me. But my wife, who would bean me before she'd put up with that sort of treatment from me, seemed to accept it in Harry's treatment of Thelma and she and Thelma are close friends.

"We walk in there, and he tells Thelma, 'Hang up their coats—don't just stand there.' She's taking her second step to the closet and he's already complaining that she hasn't offered us something to eat or drink. She just smiles, sweet as anything, and does his bidding. Meanwhile, he hasn't moved from his chair—not even to get up and shake hands.

"By the time we've left, I am so sick of Harry's voice saying 'Thelma' and so provoked with Thelma's allowing herself to be pushed around like that, I tell my wife, as I have 50 times before, that we'll never go back—or at least, I won't.

"'Why doesn't she leave him?' I asked my wife. Marcia, my wife, usually doesn't answer that question and I don't know what made her answer me then, but she said, 'I think it's because she likes hearing him say her name.'

"I think maybe we've gone over there once too often, or that maybe I've been married to Marcia for too long because, funny as it sounds, you know what? I think she's *right*."

By accepting his wife's—and Thelma's—tolerance of Harry, George allowed himself to see that a baffling relationship can have value for those maintaining it. By accepting that it suited Harry and Thelma and that his visits pleased Marcia and didn't really threaten him, Harry could let go of his displeasure and relax. In fact, he even felt enriched—and closer to his own wife after the last encounter.

It didn't matter to Thelma how Harry behaved in front of company. She obviously enjoyed living with him. George was glad for them both—and glad that neither he nor Marcia had to live with Harry. In fact, Harry made George look good, which was all right, too.

SPECIAL RELATIONSHIPS (Watch your expectations)

Some relationships are loaded with dynamite. Bosses and employees. Mothers-in-law and sons-in-law. Mothers-in-law and daughters-in-law. Mothers-in-law are legendarily difficult, critical, judgmental, inflexible, humorless troublemakers. They've been stereotyped and the staple of comedians for centuries.

Ruth and Don, married about three months, were prepared for the advent of his mother, who was coming into town from another state. It would be her first visit to their home. Don was looking forward to seeing his mother arrive. Ruth was looking forward to seeing his mother leave. She had been preparing for His Mother's

26

Inspection Tour for more than a month. The house had been cleaned to the point of nerve-straining sterility. It was so highly polished it glared blindingly. Ruth had become so insistent about neatness that Don began mentally comparing her to his old Marine Corps drill instructor.

The day—and Mom—arrived and the poor woman wore herself out delivering compliments on Ruth's appearance, her decorating sense, housekeeping skills, even her toothpaste. She was so intent on wooing and winning Ruth's affection that she was ignoring her son. Noticing a slightly hurt expression around his eyes, she reached out and, caressing his cheek, said, "Oh, my poor boy . . ." about to jokingly reassure him that she loved him as well as she loved Ruth. But Ruth cut her off by whirling around and saying, "I knew it! You never wanted him to marry me, did you?" Don and Mom were stunned, Ruth was crying.

It took some sorting out of feelings, some honest conversation, but things worked out. Sometimes, if we expect something strongly enough (rejection, on Ruth's part), we get it.

HOW TO GET OTHERS TO LIKE YOU

As Emerson said, to have a friend, you must be one. Looking for new friends can be as difficult as looking for the love of your life in a Tibetan monastery. Friendship and romance do share a few qualities and one of them is chemistry. There either is a personal, mutual "click" between people and they become friends or there isn't and they don't. When there is that

27

"click," treasure it, nurture it and thank your lucky stars for it.

You can meet new friends or a new love almost anywhere—at school, or work, attending meetings of social, professional or political organizations, shopping, attending the theater, at parties, or strolling in your neighborhood. You're not likely to meet them "alone in your room" as the theme from "Caberet" reminds you—you have to venture out of your shell, Old Chum. And when you're among them, you must let people know of your presence and let them know you are glad of theirs. *Don't* be afraid to make the first move. An old 1930s Depression song mocks such an attitude: "I ain't gonna do nothing for nobody till somebody does somethin' for me."

What qualities do you most appreciate in a friend? Among the following, put a star next to three of the characteristics you feel are absolute requirements for any friend of yours. Then check five others—only five—that you feel it would be nice for a friend to have.

outgoing	truthful
keeps a secret	independent
generous	outspoken
intelligent	gentle
shy	giving
witty	decisive
good-humored	asserting
sharing	trusting
caring	trustworthy
reliable	flexible

successful professionally
similar in background
similar goals
similar philosophies
similar interests

patient

aggressive

spontaneous

optimistic

imaginative

practical

whimsical

accessible

good listener

sympathetic

interested

supportive

encouraging

tactful

loyal

unguarded

up-to-date

well-traveled

competitive

communicative

Now, put a circle next to those qualities you feel you both possess and put to work in your friendships with others.

Friendship. It's the stuff that poems are made of and it seems to be an elusive treasure in today's world. But the very fact that there are so many of us alive and looking for friends ought to increase the odds for a match in our favor. Certainly, if not a "match," then at least a meeting should fall within the realm of probability. How many potential friends have you passed up in the past week? Are you exhibiting all the traits you say are essential to your friendships?

Are you *habitually* friendly? Good-humored? Caring? Outgoing? Interested? Open to others? If you are then you probably have more friends than you can handle. If not, perhaps you are a busy person with several preoccupations and a major full-time occupation that commands most of your attention and gives you precious little time to share with others.

Jean, at 29, had spent the last 10 years of her life making her occupation her sole preoccupation and it had paid off financially. She had come a long way since, almost exactly 10 years ago—on her 19th birthday—she had resolved to become "successful in business." Her father had run one family business after another into bankruptcy, which made survival difficult for Jean's mother, two sisters and three brothers. Jean found that the only way she could afford college was to win a scholarship. And she knew that the only way for her to succeed in business was to attend a respected university with a prestigious business college. So she got the grades and participated in the activities that helped her win the scholarship. And she kept up the grades and increased her activities (and worked as a clerk in an accounting firm) to remain on scholarship and cultivate professional references. She was recruited in her junior year by a top Wall Street firm which wooed her with promises of decent pay, upward mobility and all expenses paid to a top law school if she would pursue studies in corporate law while on the payroll. Jean accepted. She ate, slept, talked and dreamt business. As years passed, she became the young career women's idol, a favorite of the business press. Jean worked her way up to being a "business success," just as she had set out to do. Her father was properly awed, just as she had hoped he'd be. It was very satisfying, except . . . Except that she began to realize, heading for 30, that all her involvements were *professional*. Except for fleeting moments with relatives, she had no personal associations at all. She had done well, was respected and, to a degree, liked by her associates. But it was a cool degree, and Jean found she needed relationships with warmth.

It took her a while, but Jean finally came to admit that she wanted others in her life not merely because she worked with them but because she and they liked one another and wanted to spend time together. Jean knew how to handle colleagues with efficiency, but she didn't know how to achieve intimacy, to reach out for friendship. Reaching out for cooperation on a specific project, in a well-defined and recognized role is one thing; reaching out on an unofficial, person-to-person level is another. Jean was uneasy. How to start?

In one way, she had an advantage: She knew how to try for goals. She thought well of herself and gave herself the right to want—and get—what she set out for. In this case, she wanted a balance in her life, which had become too heavily work-related, too lacking in intimacy.

Instinctively, she began an informal survey, observing, among the people she knew, those who appeared to have good friends. What qualities did they all seem to share? What methods did they employ to attract and hold friends? Could she use them too?

Always an enthusiast, Jean at first went a bit overboard with hand-shaking and repeating people's names a few times too many in her attempt to let them know she remembered them and considered them important. But her motives were good and they showed through—and helped her. People *believed* the message she was telegraphing to them, which was: "I like you." "I'm interested in you." "I want to get to know you." She stopped worrying about how she was coming across and started coming across very well indeed.

"If you let people know you think well of them," said one wise person, "they might be taken aback, but they'll never question your good taste." And she is right. If you are truly interested in others, they will respond.

When you meet people for the first time or greet them on the routine rounds of your daily life, do you try to "connect" with others? Do you look them directly in the eye? Do you smile? Are you outgoing and warm or do you maintain a coolness and distance? When you are introduced, do you offer a hand in greeting? Do you shake hands? Do you really listen to a new name and repeat it and ask this new person a question or two? Try being friendlier to people—you'll like it; they'll like it too.

Be real with people and be "there." Compliment them when you mean it. If someone looks great in a new jacket, say so. If they do a good job, tell them you've noticed it and praise their work, appreciate their effort. Thank people for little favors—for taking a phone message for you, for leaving an article on your desk to read. Share new discoveries—a new restaurant, a great discount store. Bring in cookies that you bake, occasionally. Call people you'd like to know better after you've first met them. It won't hurt to try to know them better. Don't be afraid to make the first move and risk a rebuff. Let people know about you and what your interests are. But not to excess—you learn a lot more when you listen and you're most interesting when you're *interested*.

One of the best things about friends is that, however alike you may be, you are also very different and enrich one another with those differences. A friend may point out something you'd never notice—an entire city skyline reflected in an office building's glass facade, or tell you when you've got a smudge on your nose, or bring you down to earth when you need it—or soar right out in midair with you, when the timing's right.

Reach out for friendship, preferably among people of all ages. If you are rebuffed or ignored upon occasion, you'll survive it, and if you are rebuffed regularly, you—one hopes—will learn from it and revise your approach, Even rejection is a response and provides you with feedback to help you learn more about who you are and what you're doing, right or wrong. And that alone can be very useful.

SUMMARY:

Absolutely nobody is going to be able to like everybody (or even *any*body) all of the time, but you can like almost anybody some of the time. The magic formula: examine your reasons for disliking someone; accent his or her good points; find out how others feel about the individual you find so bothersome and compare your feelings with theirs—and ask yourself why they differ. Looking at the total person, questioning your reactions, will prove helpful and may reveal causes of discomfort within yourself. Meanwhile, to have a friend, you have to be one—and you have to be friendly, first of all. Liking and being liked are a reciprocal process. Liking can't be faked, but it can be cultivated as can qualities that attract people and potential friends. We people DO need people. For all their nuisance value, others enrich our lives and definitely are worth the effort required to get to know them. Even if it means risking rejection, reach out—smile, shake a hand, share an idea, ask a question, tell someone you know they are there—and that you're glad they are. Even rejection can be good for you, if you *let* it be.

CHAPTER III

HOW TO FEEL GOOD BY TURNING BAD MOMENTS INTO GOOD ONES

We cannot feel loss unless we are first fortunate enough to have something to lose. Whether we lose a loved one through death, whether we lose our good health through illness or injury, whether we lose a lover to divorce or to a rival, whether we lose a friend or a job or a promotion, loss strikes us at the emotional center of our beings, leaving some of us temporarily numb or reeling, some of us spurred to action, others of us frozen in our tracks, as if by not moving on, we will not have to deal further with this loss or with any others that might lie in waiting up ahead.

There is no "correct" way to respond to loss in your life. But there are ways to ease your pain, heal your wound, strengthen yourself to emerge stronger, if not unscathed.

If you have experienced a loss, give yourself permission to feel exactly what you are feeling. If your spouse has died, do not judge yourself to be "terrible" for feeling rage at being abandoned in this way or for feeling fear about how you will manage now, alone, without the person most influential in defining to yourself and to the world who you are.

When someone so close to you dies, it is difficult not to feel that an aspect of yourself has died. And it is essential at this point to treat yourself with loving care and understanding so that you do not deprive yourself of the gift of living—fully, richly.

Like many people, you will feel guilty for so many things—even for being alive—for surviving. Let yourself feel the guilt. Acknowledge it, let it surface. If you bottle it up it will come back again and again, unbidden, to plague you until you deal with it.

If you have regrets about things you did or didn't do, express them—don't suppress them. Again, thoughts put on the mind's back burners will boil over if not tended to. Examine your feelings and let them out—not to lacerate yourself with them, but to free yourself of them.

"If only" is a phrase we often plague ourselves with.

"If only" you had forced your spouse to see a doctor sooner.

"If only" you had (or hadn't) refused to go on that fateful trip.

"If only" you had expressed your love more often.

Now allow yourself to think other thoughts, of moments shared, of feelings expressed without words.

CHERISH THE RELATIONSHIP YOU HAD

To feel closer to the person you have lost, try to think about how he or she would want you to mourn them. Those who lived with us probably would want to tell us something like this: "My death shows that life *is* limited, yes, but that it is a gift to be used fully. Our life together was a shared gift. It would make me feel wonderful to know that sharing time with me while I was alive has enriched you enough to go on without me and to add even further to that gift of your life." Those who now love us want us to go on with our lives. They see our living fully as an affirmation of the importance of the one who has died and not a negation.

Reach out to those around you with whom you can share your feelings, or seek the aid of a religious or professional counselor or a support group—people who can, perhaps, share your memories but, even more importantly, people who can help you come to terms with your own feelings.

Your feelings of anger and loss are real. They are deep. They have been the subjects of poems, dramas, novels, paintings and songs. They aren't of the pastel sentiments found in commercial valentines, but are primal, and sometimes frightening basic emotions as old as time and life itself. The Spanish poet, José Luis Hidalgo, managed to concentrate intense, immense emotion into these brief lines from his verse, entitled "No":

> "The night crushes you so I look for you
> like a maniac in shadow, in a dream, in death.
> My heart burns up like a single bird.
> Your absence murders me, life has closed."

Because the poet releases his sorrow, grief, rage, fear, into a poem, he creates a work of art. By this creation—a poem—he does not, after all, let the other's absence "murder" him, nor does he allow life to "close" for him. He lives on and, through his work, so does the loved one and their love for one another. And by sharing how he feels, he lets others know they aren't alone in their feelings.

Not all of us are poets. But all of us could profit from this advice, from William Shakespeare:

> "Give sorrow words; the grief that does not
> speak whispers the o'er fraught heart
> and bids it break."

As the survivor, your health—mental, physical and emotional—is at the mercy not so much of outside circumstances as of the state of peace or turmoil within yourself. Allow yourself to have the feelings you have and you eventually will resolve them peacefully. Try to deny their existence and they will struggle until you deal with them.

Your feeling that you have lost your identity because of a loved one's death is frightening. It is also based in reality. You are no longer John or Jane's spouse. You are the widow or widower of John or Jane. But who *else* are you? Who else will you *become?*

ENDINGS CAN BE BEGINNINGS TOO

If you allow yourself to be someone who can reach out to others you will find that the ending marked by this death that has left you so bereft is also a beginning. You can start on a new journey—better prepared than ever before, thanks to the experience and memories of preceding years to help you chart your new course. Or, you can stay frozen in your tracks, pretending nothing has changed, avoiding change in your imagination but, in reality, becoming more and more changed, more and more entrenched in your refusal to change. It is said that it takes a lifetime to prepare for death and certainly, all that has gone before us has prepared us for the moments that lie in our future.

Mary's lifetime had not prepared her well for Richard's death. She had been used to living her life according to the prescriptions of others—first her parents' and then her husband's.

Mary and Richard had been married for 47 years when, after a brief and sudden illness, Richard died. Alone, with no surviving relatives or friends, though she had spent all 72 years of life in this town, she knew no one. Even the lawyer who handled the estate was a stranger and had succeeded the old attorney who had known hers and Richard's families for years. Because he was the only being around who even offered her advice, she followed his urgings to sell the house that had been her home for nearly half a century and moved to a new apartment complex. She hoped she would meet people and make new friends as he had predicted. But she seldom saw anyone—most all the tenants worked—and only occasionally on a Saturday would she meet anyone at the mailboxes in the lobby. By accident she met—and was befriended by a young woman on her floor. The younger woman invited Mary to tea and in for lunch a few times and even dinner, when her husband, who worked late, wasn't home. Soon Mary overresponded, by ringing her neighbor's doorbell at all hours—until she heard the woman's husband complain about the intrusions. After that, Mary withdrew. About a year of bitter isolation followed before Mary was found dead by the building's superintendent. She had died alone in an apartment building full of people, unknown by any in the town of her birth.

Joanna's lifetime prepared her differently for the death of Fred, to whom she had been married for 45 years.

Fred had been stricken by a heart attack while he and Joanna were vacationing in Las Vegas, a town previously unknown to either of them. He died two weeks later. During his illness, Joanna was a stranger in a strange town, reluctant to wire her grown children, who were abroad on vacation at the time, hoping Fred would be fine. She called her sisters—and Fred's brother—but assured them (and herself) that he would be all right. She reached out to nurses, one of whom insisted on Joanna's moving into her home and out of the hotel at which she and Fred had been staying. Joanna offered friendship to and accepted it from visitors attending to other patients on the floor and with them talked through lonely vigils in the night. When Fred died, Joanna notified family and friends and when she arrived at her hometown airport with his coffin, was glad to be met by caring faces. She spoke of her grief and others responded but when she felt she was burdening them, she spoke instead to her pastor and to members of a support group in the area. When she felt lonely, she recalled memories of the good times shared with Fred. When she had to make decisions, she asked herself, "What would Fred have done?" Often, she said, it felt as though he was there, helping her, despite his death. A bit over a year later, Joanna married again. Said her pastor: "Her marriage is a tribute to Fred, an acknowledgement by Joanna that they had found marriage too valuable to live without."

Death is not the only cause of the loss of a partner. Sometimes, when we find out about infidelity and "the other"—man or woman—death can appear almost a preferable alternative to betrayal. In your pain, you might wish for death. Initially for the rival, then for the unfaithful spouse or mate, and later, in the pain of struggle and acceptance, for yourself. Most people survive this pain and are glad of it, after all.

Many a sad song or verse laments the loss of love and probably none is quoted oftener than this verse of Tennyson's:

" 'Tis better to have loved and lost
Than never to have loved at all."

He is quoted with good reason.

If you have loved and lost and experienced the initial joys of loving and being loved as well as the pain of loving and losing, you have shared in one of life's richest adventures. You have learned that winning is better than losing, if nothing else, and eventually, you will want to try your hand at winning once again.

ASK YOURSELF WHY YOU LOST

To benefit from this lost labor of love and to prepare yourself for a new beginning, examine the reasons for this romance's ending. Don't go over all the mistakes you may have made to plague yourself, but to help yourself understand what happened.

Looking back, can you see that by pretending there were no problems between you, you helped the problems to grow? In all relationships there are trouble spots and clues to what is causing them, signs that they are forming or about to materialize. You may not have faced them then but, by taking advantage of hindsight, you can increase your awareness of your own behavior and reactions for next time. By facing our mistakes now, we increase our chance of avoiding them next time.

Death is an ending. Divorce is an ending. Breaking up with a lover for whatever reason is an ending. Endings are generally associated with loss and sadness. But they can also signal new beginnings, if you allow them to. Though never easy to bear, such endings do afford you an opportunity to begin again, to redefine yourself, to reconstruct your life.

Think of all that had been good about the relationship. Think of all you would like to recreate from it. Think of all you would like to have from another relationship that you did not have in the previous one. Then recall all the non-desirable aspects of the old relationship that you would not want to repeat. Try to evaluate what YOU contributed to both the good and the bad. Now make your plans to, in your next relationship, increase the desirable qualities as much as possible and diminish or delete the undesirable ones. The possibilities for happiness in new beginnings are what keep us so fond of our tomorrows.

Sharon found out that endings and beginnings were less to be feared than she once had thought:

Sharon and John had been married for three years when he came home and announced that he had "had" it. She had been aware of some distance between them, but had not realized a rival had entered the picture. Within two hours of serving "notice," John moved out on Sharon and in with the other woman. Devastated at first, Sharon picked herself up and began to put back the pieces of her shattered life. "It hurt—a lot," she says. "But it has been good for me too, surprisingly. For one thing, John always was ridiculing my dreams of being able to design for a fashion house. I had tons of sketches and would talk of trying for a job. He told me to forget my college ambitions and stick to secretarial work— it paid steadily. He said I'd never be able to compete successfully. I believed him or, at any rate, didn't want to annoy him; I stayed at my secretarial job, but still did designs; sewing, too, sometimes. Two weeks after John left, I had set up appointments for job interviews at half a dozen places—and I wore my designs to the interviews. Now I'm an apprentice and though the money isn't great, it's as good as I was making—and I'm doing what I always dreamed of doing. He said it couldn't be done—ha!—and I did it."

MATERIAL LOSS—FACING FACTS

Regardless of how we categorize it, loss hurts. Certainly loss of a job or of a promised promotion on the job is a blow to our professional pride, our self-esteem and our ability to provide for ourselves and our families. We can choose to learn from our mistakes or to repeat them again and again. We can gear ourselves for action or wallow in fear or self-pity or self-disgust and brand ourselves "losers." We don't always think so, but the choice is ours.

Joe walked out of George's office thin-lipped and ashen. He had just been chewed out and threatened with demotion. "Ever since your tenure, Joe, you've let things slide. You just seem to get more and more careless and you've always got some excuse—it's always somebody else's fault. When I get called on the carpet by the guys upstairs for the sloppiness of your work, I can't say 'It's Joe's fault.' I have to take the criticism and tell those people I won't let it happen again. But you never tell me that. If you're not going to try to figure out how you can do better—without trying to figure out how to blame everybody else—then maybe you shouldn't be here. I can't afford to keep looking bad. Shape up, or you're not going to be top man in your area anymore." Later, Joe told a co-worker: "I'm sick of it. These bosses are all the same. I've been through four of them now, and they all abuse their power, treat me like dirt. I keep getting my hopes up, everytime we get a new one, but it's always the same story. They're all alike."

After his dressing down, Joe responded by drinking four straight vodkas at lunch—he was fond of saying no one can smell vodka, but everybody could. He talked of going on job interviews. And he clipped ads out of the paper and left them in plain sight on his desk, hoping the boss would see. (The boss did see—and *hoped* Joe would get another job.) Joe complained about the unfairness of his lot. But he never changed it. And his current boss was right—Joe had never asked even one of his previous bosses *HOW* he could improve or change. And he turned a deaf ear to any signals that *he* could change and improve his situation. Joe long ago decided to view himself as a victim— a pawn in the hands of management. He hasn't noticed that, though his bosses have changed, their complaints about him have remained unchanged. And so have his responses to them.

Have you been bypassed for promotion? Perhaps it is time to look for another job. It may also be time to look at your method of operation. Is it a lot like Joe's? Review the situation—to learn something, not merely to gripe about it—and to take a look at how you respond to criticism, how willing you are to change. Perhaps you are doing all the right things to gain your *real* goal—to *NOT* be promoted.

How much of your boss's evaluation about you was true?

How hard did you really try to meet the requirements for that promotion?

44

If you did try to meet demands and standards—and if you made every effort to understand and meet the expectations placed on you, if your boss's evaluation was total hogwash and you know it, it may be that you *are* being unfairly edged out. On the other hand, if you *didn't* really try, perhaps you should now try to do as well as you can in the job you have and work as hard as possible to land a better one elsewhere. But, for heaven's sake, keep your "looking" quiet.

Joe, who liked the role of Loser/Victim, often spoke around the office of new job possibilities and offers he had received for great money—and sometimes his stories were true. Nobody, however, seemed to follow through and actually hire him, but Joe never talked about that. He would feel better about himself when telling his co-workers about his near-successes in the job market and he wanted his SOB of a boss to hear them too.

Joe liked to say, "Some day, they're not going to have me to push around anymore." But Joe liked being pushed around. And if the newest boss could content himself with pushing Joe around every once in a while, then nothing much would change, particularly Joe. And that would suit him fine.

Do you want to take on Joe's story as your own? You didn't get your promotion. Do you want to settle for what is, to accept THE END as punctuation on your long-held hope? If you know you did well, despite what the boss says, one of you has warped vision. If you've tried your best but have run up against a dead end, then you can either make the best of it or look for something better. Probably you know which course you have to take. Eileen did:

45

Eileen had been evaluated and put on 90 days' probation. She pretended to be surprised at this, but wasn't really. She had seen it coming for months, ever since the new boss had come in 18 months ago. He had let it be known he didn't like her style and that he wanted to bring in his own people. He had been giving her the dregs of the departmental work and, she had to admit, she hadn't been giving it her full effort. For one thing, it didn't seem worth it and, for another, she'd known after about three months on the job— taken two years ago—that she had made a mistake; that she was in the wrong place at the wrong time. She kept the evaluation and the notice to herself, maintained a cheerful facade at work and began calling people she knew for leads. She updated her résumé and made the rounds of agencies. She thought, "90 days . . . sounds like a jail sentence. But it will go quickly. I've got to get moving."

Like many of us, Eileen knew the truth but wouldn't admit it until she absolutely had to. We try to fool ourselves. Usually, bad things happen when we fool ourselves. Once we face facts, we have a chance to make really good things happen.

WHEN BAD THINGS BUNCH UP, TAKE GOOD CARE OF YOURSELF

When things seem to be going wrong at work, it is often a good idea to lay low, stay quiet, listen a great deal and make few or no waves. Try to calm yourself and reinforce your feelings about your abilities. Do what you can to meet your job's requirements and it might improve your standing and increase the good opinion others have about you, your good opinion of yourself and—also important—your references. Don't burn any bridges here; the only one you'll hurt will be you if you do.

Concentrate on conserving your energy, on thinking clearly, on looking as good as possible. Do this because you deserve to look and feel as good as possible.

Bad things do happen in clumps when we are in a state of low energy and poor perception. Sometimes one failure occurs at an especially vulnerable moment and we feel defeated. With our defenses down and our vulnerability high, preoccupied with how badly we feel, we allow other bad things to happen and there is a snowball effect. It can happen with SNAFUS hitting all levels—work and love and stockmarket investments and burning the teakettle and catching the flu and being mugged—and all in the same week.

Taking good care of yourself at such times is of major importance. Proper rest, a sensible diet and some vitamin supplements would be a good idea.

Have fun, spend time with people who you know care about you. Do something you always wanted to do (take flying lessons?). Buy yourself something nice. Plan a future treat.

Part of being good to yourself is taking advantage of as much good as possible in the circumstances of your life. The happiest people habitually make lemonade out of life's lemons. You may recall:

- Richard died and left Mary alone and, after 27 years of depending on him for her identity, poor Mary found it impossible to go on. She died within a year, alone and unutterably lonely.

- When Fred's death ended his 30-year marriage to Joanna, she did what she had always done—she reached out to people and took what warmth and comfort she could from them. She said she even allowed Fred's spirit to help her and felt, when she remarried a year later, that she had his blessings as well as everyone else's.

- Susan, devastated at John's sudden and brutal goodbye as he walked out of their marriage and into the arms of another woman, ultimately made the best of her plight. With John no longer around to discourage her career aspirations, she pursued a dream and is on her way to making it come true.

- Joe, warned that he might be demoted for placing blame on others instead of asking how he can avoid mistakes, now blames bosses generally for picking on him. He doesn't notice that, though the bosses have changed, their complaints are the same. He has opted for the role of victim. He is used to it and doesn't want to change. He has gotten used to lemons.

Allen however, never did care much for lemons. His story is worth recounting:

An automobile accident transformed Allen from a star college football player to a young man with one leg. He was despondent at first, and uncertain about what to do with the rest of his life. His career plans had gone down the drain. He figured, after years of pro football, he'd become a coach and stay in the game till he was old and gray. But now, his Dad wanted him to join the family accounting firm. Allen knew his father meant well, but resisted the offer. Allen had always believed in going after what you really wanted. He was going to take a little time and decide what he really wanted. For three months after he had recuperated, Allen returned regularly to the hospital, visiting with handicapped youngsters, teaching them about sports. He also did volunteer work as a coach at a nearby school. Finally, Allen knew what he wanted to do with his life: He returned to college, and became a physical therapist. He has spent the last five years working with physically handicapped youngsters, emphasizing not only the importance of good therapy but the good therapy of athletics. He and the youngsters are a happy combination.

When life has dealt you a blow, you might need to lie there for a while just to regain your equilibrium, but then you must get up again and move on. Reach out for a hand to help you up—and take one if it's offered or ask for one if it isn't.

Take your own inventory of all your strengths. Then call upon them to help you get through. Banish all doubts about your ability to succeed. Congratulate yourself for standing on your feet again which includes reaching out for help. Map a plan for your future progress, and carry it out one step at a time.

Calling upon all you have learned about liking yourself (Chapter I) and all you've mastered about liking others (Chapter II) reach out to the qualities in others that can prove most helpful now, in your bad moments.

Set reachable goals for yourself—but don't be afraid to stretch to reach them, a little farther each day, until you get what you're aiming at.

By living through the worst of times we often learn about the best there is in ourselves and in others. We come to salute our ability to endure—and to celebrate ourselves and others and life itself.

SUMMARY:

Loss can be devastating but, with determination and belief in our ability to do so, we can turn bad moments into good ones. Death of one we love is frightening and final and inspires our anger, fear, sorrow, our feelings of abandonment, aloneness and guilt. By acknowledging all of these we can learn much about ourselves and can use this knowledge to strive for balance in our lives. In losses other than death, when we feel most bereft, we should assess what we have lost and why—to learn from our mistakes and avoid repeating them. Recognizing the warning signals of troubles in relationships is one way to head off trouble and unwanted endings. Every ending is sad and entails a loss of some sort. But endings need not be the end of you. They also can be an opprotunity for new starts.

Allow yourself a healing time, a time to develop a peace within yourself, and a plan to follow. And then, follow that plan with all the discipline and determination and faith in yourself and life that it is possible for you to muster. You can achieve any reasonable goal you believe you can achieve. And that achievement will lead you on to others.

Call on all that is meaningful to you—your love for others, your faith—your belief in the possibilities of life—and put them to work to accomplish what you feel you must.

Losses, endings, bad moments, good new starts, they are all part and parcel of the game of life and, as Yogi Berra is credited with having said: "The game isn't over till it's over." Keep on playing. And play to win.

CHAPTER IV

HOW TO FEEL GOOD BY EXCHANGING OLD OUTDATED HABITS FOR GOOD NEW ONES

All is flux, nothing stands
still. Nothing endures but
change.—Heraclitus 540–580 BC

You must do the thing you think you
cannot do.—Eleanor Roosevelt

Bad habits are like two-sided swords with danger-ously sharp cutting edges. We developed them as tools and weapons to ease our lives or to protect ourselves but find ourselves victimized by them instead.

All bad habits are methods we have devised for not facing our real feelings. They are deflective shields that keep us from knowing who we really are, what we're really capable of, what *life* really is.

Generally, we develop a bad habit to avoid discom-fort or to ease the pressure of painful situations. A drink to relax. A cookie to sweeten a tearful child's bit-ter moment, a splurge purchase to keep our minds off how tight our finances are. A little exaggeration about our vacation accommodations to make our trip appear more glamorous and to add interest to the tale.

The drinks increase, the relaxation doesn't. The cookies mount and are replaced by mounds of food—and flesh—as the child ages and grows in girth. The splurge serves to add to our preoccupation with our ever-tightening, frightening budget situation. The constant need to exaggerate ultimately makes us less real to ourselves. (What was wrong with living in a gardener's cottage? Why pretend to be the live-in friend of an English earl with a 500-acre estate? The aftertaste of a fib can sour an actually sweet experience.)

A bad habit is one with a generally negative effect that outweighs any satisfaction we might get from it. And satisfaction (escape from discomfort) is what prompted its adoption in the first place.)

Ironically, all bad habits are both self-indulgent and self-destructive. They are self-indulgent because we engage in them to become preoccupied with self rather than face head-on a bad feeling or an unpleasant moment. Actually, since we respond with feelings to whatever occurs around us, we can't truly avoid the feeling evoked from good or bad moments. If we express our feelings about them—to ourselves—if we deal directly with what happens and assimilate it, "it" assumes its proper place in our lives and we move on. If we suppress our response to what has happened, the undealt with unpleasant moments pile up within our unconsciousness and stop us or slow us down. The stilled responses, the unfaced moments, accumulate to assume monumental proportions and become far more important than they might be.

Unpleasant moments are a part of life. How we respond to them adds up to the life we live. Do we face their challenges as learning experiences or do we shy away from them? Do we live life or hide from its risks?

Bad habits are hiding places that grow with our unacknowledged fears. At full-growth, they sprout enormous billboards announcing, "Here's where X hides, housed in fear." X might not notice the sign. But everybody else does.

There are at least three kinds of bad habits, which we put into the following categories:

I. *Conscious Symptomatic Relief Responses*

Those habits *we are aware* of and *say we would like to give up* but *don't*, because we adopted them in the first place to satisfy particular needs (ease or escape from discomfort). We keep the bad habits, even though we know they are bad for us—even though they result in our feeling badly—because initially, we indulged in them to make ourselves feel good and at the moment that we engage in them they make us feel good by relieving the pain.

Some Category I Habits: Eating junk food, smoking, drinking too much, overspending, underspending, overeating, gambling.

II. *Unconscious Psychodynamic Responses*

Habits in this category are those of which *we are aware* and annoyed with but to which we have *become attached*. They may have been picked up unconsciously and probably are related to a specific anxiety.

Some Category II Habits: Compulsions such as hand-washing, constant cleaning, sloppiness, being too early for appointments, lateness, not bathing, general procrastination.

III. *Unconscious Tension Responses*

Habits in this category are those of which we are *not aware*. They may be distracting or disturbing to others or may interfere with our best performance.

Some Category III Habits: Head-scratching, knee-jerking, repeating stories, teeth-clicking, tuning out on others, sniffling, not concentrating, lying, interrupting others, forgetfulness.

As we have said before, change is probably the most frightening of concepts. We carry around old habits the way a cartoon child carries his security blanket. But he's supposed to *stay* a child forever. We're supposed to grow up. Life is to live, not to avoid. Fears are to be faced and joys to be cherished. There are feelings of pride to experience because of our efforts—not just our successes but more importantly, our *efforts*—to give and get as much as we can from this life of ours. Pride in having tried, in having learned, in having gotten a little wiser and stronger by encountering life head-on instead of seeking refuge from it in eating, drinking, spending or whatever avoidance mechanism that's employed to avoid head-on confrontations with reality.

Do you want to change or eliminate a habit? Then first, give yourself credit for being able to handle the painful feelings. If you admit you feel them, you will loosen some of their hold on you. If you deal with them, rather than try to avoid the hurt they *might* cause, you can possibly devise a plan that will change your responses to painful elements in your life, making you less vulnerable, more in charge.

Meanwhile, remember back in Chapter I—how you agreed that you must love yourself before you can learn to love others and accept their love for you? All right, so you don't always fall madly in love with yourself overnight. Try for like. Instant self-like. Unconditional self-like. You are alive now. Live your life now. Not, "after I lose the weight." Not, "after I quit drinking." Not, "after I manage my budget for a year." Not "after" anything. Now.

If you like yourself, you'll help yourself reach out for life rather than hide from it via your habit. You'll allow yourself to have far more than life under that anesthesia supplied by booze or drugs or food or whatever. You'll even say you are worth more. The kowtowing to fear of pain, the anesthesia of the habit to ease the fear of the fear, the self-recriminations after you've once again turned to the habit and away from true feelings— these are keeping you in chains. In *The Little Prince*, by Antoine St. Exupery the little hero encounters a drunk, who is crying:

"Why are you unhappy?" asks the Little Prince.
"Because I drink."
"Why do you drink?"
"Because I am unhappy."

If we would look at what it is in life that evokes our feelings of fear or unhappiness, if we confronted the dragons within ourselves, we would break the locks on the cells we have forged for ourselves. We could get out of the vicious cycle, the circular rut that gets us nowhere new. The only fairy godmother you've got is you.

Cast your own magic spell. Give yourself a kiss—transform yourself into a beauty, a royal figure—get rid of the green warts. Sing a little and stop croaking.

"But," you croak. "Breaking habits is hard to do."

Starting is probably the hardest part. The more you exercise, the easier it gets. The more you practice a habit, the more automatic it becomes.

"I've been doing this for so long," says the frog/person. "I'll start, last a week and it'll be all over."

What will be "all over?" Commitment means seeing an effort through—it doesn't mean no failures. It doesn't mean instant success. Facing your fears doesn't mean instant victory, either. It means being afraid and saying "I am afraid." It means examining why you're afraid, instead of backing away and running to hide in your habit. It means trying new approaches to problems instead of following the same old escape route. It means failing. Change means effort. Effort can make you uncomfortable. It can also make you feel proud—like a person, instead of a frog. Some things to try: Buy some flowers *instead* of a junk food snack, a facial *instead* of a fifth of spirits, volunteer to work with youngsters *instead* of shopping.

The three categories of habits we outlined earlier may or may not contain one or more of your own bad habits. Certainly, they are engaged in by millions who often say they want to "get rid of them" but somehow never get started. There are, however, millions of others who have succeeded, sometimes temporarily, sometimes permanently, to kick their unwanted habits.

Here are some suggestions to strengthen your habit-kicking, whatever the category:

1. Choose one habit that you are going to eliminate.

2. Really examine that habit. Try to remember when you first realized it *was* a habit. Can you recall a time when you knew it was more than some behavior you resorted to "once in a while?" What situations usually trigger your response to indulge the habit? What feelings make you so uncomfortable that you use the habit as a distraction from them?

3. Forget about blaming Mom or Uncle Charley for introducing you to your first bite or that first drink to help ease a painful moment. Face the fact that you're not a tot, that you're responsible for your own life and for making it work. Admit that this habit is not helping you and that for that reason only, you have chosen to drop it from your repertory. Then map out how you plan to do it.

4. Resolve to go beyond treating your symptoms with your habit and to treat the ailment—fear of facing painful or tense moments, loneliness, anger, disappointment, rejection, or whatever. Resolve to face those feelings and give yourself the right to have them.

5. When you first feel the urge to indulge in your bad habit, ask yourself what inspired it? (Did you miss the bus to work and arrive late? Did your lunch date fall through? Did your boss criticize you? Did good old Mom get your goat? Did you *not* get invited to a party? Express verbally, to a friend, or in writing to yourself, what you felt about any incidents—how they seemed threatening or disturbing. Are you terrible for feeling anger or resentment? Are you a crybaby for feeling hurt? Isn't it perfectly understandable that you would feel as you do at such unpleasant happenings? Isn't it human? Are you feeling less than saintly as a result of

such responses? Why should you be perfect? Human will do nicely! Now that you have looked at the enemy —these fearsome feelings—can you allow yourself to have them? Can you begin to work at understanding them—and yourself? And can you see that facing these feelings—can help, rather than destroy you? Ask yourself questions. Give yourself answers. Listen to yourself. Get to know you.

If, after all that dialogue, you can also ask whether resorting to your habit would have changed the situation, do so. You might find that by not *hiding*, that by facing the feeling you usually avoid, you won't feel like running. At least not this time. If you still are tempted to employ the habit, tell yourself that just this once, I won't.

Now for more specialized methods to kick bad habits, category by category:

Dealing with Habits in Category #1 (overeating, overspending, drinking and smoking too much, etc.)

TREATMENT TECHNIQUE #1

Cold Turkey. Throw away your last pack of cigarettes. Go on a fast. Close out your charge accounts. Drink only club soda. This technique to kick a habit works best for the highly addictive person, the person who responds to a tough challenge or one who likes to do things in the extreme.

TREATMENT TECHNIQUE #2

The Slow Wind-Down. This approach is best for those interested in establishing rational controls. It appeals most to those who would never intentionally take a cold shower, go hang-gliding or play strip poker.

1. Monitor yourself for three days.

2. Jot down the day and date, time, place and occurrence and reason for indulging in the habit.

3. After three days, look over your list and determine which of those occasions were really unnecessary even for your needs. (For example, you really did not enjoy the piece of pie you ate before you went to bed . . . Lighting a cigarette before you get up for the day is automatic, rather than a desire . . . Having a cocktail at lunch makes you drowsy—not happy and alert—a handicap in your work.")

4. Spend the next three days eliminating all unnecessary occurrences of engaging in your habit. Continue to note when, where and why (and with whom) you practice the bad habit.

5. Review your notes to determine which 50 percent of the times you engage in your habit can be eliminated. Knowing you can still look forward to some indulgences of the habit should help counter feelings of deprivation.

6. Monitor your behavior for the next seven days, engaging in your bad habits only half as often as you did in the beginning. Continue keeping notes.

7. Review your notes and determine to eliminate 25 percent more of all indulgences in your bad habit for the next seven days.

8. At the end of this last seven-day period, decide if you want to live with this habit at this 25 percent level of practice because you feel you are in control of it and it is no longer a bad habit. Or decide that you want to proceed until you have eliminated it completely.

Dealing with Habits in Category #2

Although unconscious, these bad habits sometimes may be easier to eliminate than those in Category #1 because many of these habits are just that—habits. They may stem from childhood and no longer serve a purpose, along the lines of that ritualistic "Step on a crack, break your mother's back" observance. Some 48-year-old "kids" still won't step on cracks but long ago forgot why. (These habits include constant hand-washing or cleaning, sloppiness, general procrastination.)

If you don't have some of these habits, you probably know someone who does. For instance, there's the kind of person who empties the ash tray as soon as you use it. Or the other extreme—the one who lives in an extremely messy home—you've been there—remember, the living room in which you had to step over piles of newspapers to get to the sofa?

These habits may be their owners' ways of copying (or rebelling against) their parents. However understandable the behavior may have been when they were nine-year-olds, these habitués are performing rituals no longer meaningful: They are adults living in their own homes. As an adult you can tell yourself what to do. You can set your own standards. You needn't live up to—or rebel against—Mom's.

Try to persuade Robert of that:

Robert always resented his mother's sloppiness and her lack of concerned housekeeping. He vowed he never would keep his home like that. Indeed, he has gone to the opposite extreme.

Everyone who enters Robert's home has to leave his or her shoes in the front entry hall. No smoking is allowed. All dishes are put away immediately after they've been used.

And then there's Richard:

Richard resented his mother's controlling cleanliness and purposely avoids keeping his apartment neat. His clothes leave a trail from foyer through living room and into the bedroom. Dishes get washed only when there are none left in the cupboard.

And Joan's story goes this way:

Joan hates her own obsession with perfection but, compulsively, she must arrange all nicknacks in their exact spot, wash all dishes the moment they've been used (she even does this in other people's homes). She is frustrated by her own compulsion and doesn't understand her overpowering urge to persist in it. What she doesn't realize is that she originally developed these habits as a child to protect herself and her home from bad luck. She doesn't even remember how she developed this idea, but persists with the superstition, even though she no longer feels the need for this superstitious protection ritual. People who need things done in an exact way feel they are protecting the order of things in their lives. The truth is, if they took the risk and stopped the rituals, life would go on, the world would turn and misfortune would not befall them as a result.

Robert, Richard and Joan all share one fear—the fear of giving up their childhood rituals. The treatment is to slowly eliminate the compulsive repetition of the procedure. For example. Robert might start by leaving one (clean) dish in the sink overnight. And he might resist the urge to pick up all those little specks of lint off the carpet after he has vacuumed—by leaving the room immediately.

The secret of ridding yourself of these bad habits is to realize that you can feel comfortable without performing the rituals—and that nothing bad will happen to you (or others) because of it. Take it slowly, a step at a time, so you'll be comfortable.

Another Category #2 habit that is inspired by the dominant need to avoid tension or discomfort is procrastination. The procrastinator appears at every social and professional level imaginable. He or she works harder than anyone else you know—at avoiding feelings of inadequacy or pressure over an impending deadline. The deadline could involve picking up clothes at the cleaners before 2 p.m. Saturday, finishing a report for the department head, meeting friends for a movie date or handing in a term paper on time, memorizing a speech, putting the dinner-party roast into the oven by 7 p.m. or paying your taxes before the midnight deadline on April 15. Some procrastinators will say they do this sort of thing because they are lazy—thus removing responsibility for this behavior from themselves. Some say they fear the completed work is falling short of a perfectionistic goal. (Undone work remains potentially perfect.) Others say they are snidely rebelling against authority—being late shows a sort of sneer. (It also shows compliance—the task is done, just the deadline is unmet.) Doctors lose patients by being late. Employees lose promotion points for being late. Businesses lose millions because promised products are delivered late. Some people lose their lives by putting off medical care or automobile repairs.

Procrastinators seem to have one common characteristic: They are all living under pressure, experiencing the mental harangue that urges them to get the undone done. Perhaps it is a way of keeping the parental voice playing constantly, an affirmation that one's childhood is not really over, after all. The harangue (and resistance to it) are energy-draining. The Little Prince might have met a procrastinator and asked the same questions of him or her that he asked of the drunk:

"Why are you so worried?"
"Because I have so much work undone."
"Then why don't you do it?"
"Because I'm so worried."

At the bottom of things, we are what we *do*. If what we do is devote our time to not doing things on time, people will come to know us for that trait. Some will accept it in us and act accordingly. (Procrastinators are often so notorious that hostesses invite them for dinner at 5 p.m., knowing they'll arrive at 6:30. Dinner actually is for 7). Or they will invite them for drinks and coffee at 8 p.m., knowing they'll turn up after the dinner table has been cleared and the prompt guests have been dined and wined. Others will drop us entirely. Some hostesses won't invite procrastinators at all.

We can't hold back time by holding back on action. In a tragicomic sort of way, the procrastinator does perfect something—his or her own ability to turn an ordinary situation into a reason to worry. The procrastinator may resist and resent the pressure a deadline or an appointment presents but these are minor compared with the pressures self-imposed while resisting them.

By working hard to keep things unchanging, we change all the same, if only by becoming more and more the person our actions make of us.

Dealing with Habits in Category #3

Sometimes, merely becoming aware of our behavior is enough to help us overcome it. Perhaps the biggest problem here is a tremendous resistance to acknowledging that we have this bad habit. The habits in this category include head-scratching, knee-jerking, sniffling, teeth-clicking, repeating stories, tuning out on others, interrupting others' conversations, being forgetful, nail-biting, hair-twisting, soup-slurping and saying "ummm" and "er" as you talk.

If constant reminders from others have begun to persuade you that you just *might* have a problem, try running a tape cassette, recording yourself as you eat soup or tell a story. Or you might make a note of it everytime you are told that you are interrupting someone or that you forgot a birthday, anniversary, holiday, dinner date, your boss's name or your umbrella—again.

Another approach you might try is this:

If you discover that you have a habit that you seem unable to consciously control, there is a very good behavior modification technique called "repetition" that has proven helpful in eliminating physical mannerisms such as teeth-clicking, sniffling and the like.

It's simple enough to employ and here's how it works:

Force yourself to engage in this bad habit consciously and deliberately for a 10-minute period. You will find yourself exhausted by having to force yourself to do this very behavior you've been criticized for and that you've been denying to yourself actually is a habit. If you repeat this method at 10-minute intervals for one hour, doing it becomes a negative experience and you extinguish the habit.

SUMMARY:

Breaking outdated habits that no longer serve or satisfy your need to feel better (when you perform them you often feel worse) is not easy. It also is not impossible. Instead of feeling deprived by not eating that bowl of oatmeal at 3:30 a.m. (swimming with butter and sugar and cream because it was the only edible left in the kitchen) and you felt the urge because it was Saturday night and nobody had asked you out (again)—you can feel free of the mania to munch. How? By daring to feel the emotion you're trying to tamp down your throat with food. Let yourself feel what you feel— sad, angry, rejected. Cry—let the sounds and the anger up, instead of pushing them back down with food. And once you've expressed it, be glad that you haven't added calorie fuel to your body, which will give it a chance to burn the calories already stored within it. To make yourself feel better, buy flowers, not food, cologne or a blouse or shirt. Get a new hairstyle. go to a movie or a play, not a restaurant or supermarket. Phone a friend or a shut-in instead of the pizza-pie guy. Take a walk around town. Look at clothes in smaller sizes at the stores and imagine how great you'll be looking in them. Postpone your urge to bite or imbibe or to gamble or to buy something that will break your budget's back and make you feel even worse than you did before. If you can put it off for five minutes, put if off for 15. Trade your bad habit for good company or exercise or a lovely fantasy of life without the habit, without the fear that you "can't handle" the discomforts of life. Don't avoid the reality of how you feel—which is why you formed the habit in the first place— but face that reality. Feel that emotion. You're stronger and smarter and better than you dreamed —and every time you succeed at handling your feelings of discomfort, you'll feel freer—deprived not of an indulgence that gives you instant pleasure, but of shackles that keep you down.

Perhaps most important is to give yourself the right to govern yourself. Don't follow patterns just because you're used to them. Don't follow rules set for you by others long ago. Don't scold yourself or nag yourself because your parents did. Be the parent to your adult self that you wished you'd had as a child. And be the adult you've spent your life wanting to become—it's time to grow up and it can be fun.

CHAPTER V

HOW TO FEEL GOOD BY
MAKING STRESS WORK FOR YOU

Stress is a physiological response to internal and external physical or emotional pressures. Hans Selye, the pioneer in stress exploration, called it a "general adaptation syndrome"—the body's biochemical means for coping with outside stimuli.

It might help us to understand how stress acts upon our body if we think of the way a rubber band expands when it it stretched: Initially, there is an easy give. As the tension increases, and the reserve rubber becomes used up, the strain becomes apparent until, if the pressure continues, the rubber band breaks under the stress. And this is similar to the ways in which we respond. In itself, stress is neither good nor bad. It merely signals a change in our situation. In fact, studies show that stress increases satisfaction and productivity—up to a point. Then, like the rubber band, the intensity of the pressure and our ability to adapt to it determines if this is "good" stress or "bad" stress. This has given rise to a distinction between "Eustress" which refers to stress that is converted to positive energy and gives us the drive to try harder and reach for higher goals; and "Distress" in which stress is converted into negative energy resulting in feelings of fatigue and defeat. It is "Distress" which results in the destructive biochemical changes leading to physical ailments.

"Eustress vs. Distress"

Attitude is everything in determining whether we use stress to give us more energy and drive or to overwhelm us into passivity and defeat.

> Bonnie and Mike are vying for the same promotion. They have been at the same company for a little over a year and were both hired with the expectation of promotion and growth with this young developing company. They have put in the many hours of overtime required and are both in line for the new vice-presidency spot being created. The next few months will determine who gets that spot. Bonnie is resentful of being placed in this competitive role. She has a good relationship with Mike and enjoys working with him. She feels that she has put in enough overtime and enough hours of hard work to prove her ability and dedication. Her resentment has increased the anger and fatigue that she feels and she realizes that she has begun to slow up at work and find excuses to not stay late. Feeling angry at work makes her unhappy about living alone and not having someone special in her life to help her. Her initial excitement and enthusiasm about the challenge and potential of this new job has, under

69

the increased pressure of competition, converted "Eustress" into "Distress."

Mike, on the other hand, understands that the competition that has been created between him and Bonnie is a common company ploy to get each of them to work even harder and show their best. He understands that competition is part of the game and does not feel this will affect his good relationship with Bonnie. Only one of them will get promoted this time but the other one will have another opportunity soon, probably at this company, if not, at another. Mike thinks the game is silly but he is not angry at the company for it. In fact, he is grateful for the pressure because he has discovered abilities and stamina in himself that he didn't know he had! He also lives alone but is glad of it! When he comes home from work at 10 p.m. he wants to be by himself and relax without having to be concerned about another person. He sees his present situation as a temporary, total commitment to succeeding at this job. This is his first goal and he will tackle his other goals later.

In spite of the increased pressure, Mike has been able to maintain his feeling of "Eustress" by channelling his reactions and responses in certain directions:

1. One focused goal

2. Objectivity about company demands and policy

3. Lack of guilt regarding competition

4. Time limited expectation of this intense stress situation

Since stress is a response to change, it is clear that our attitude toward change and our ability to adapt to new situations is the single most important indicator of whether we experience stress as "Eustress" (good) or "Distress" (bad). Certainly a primary source of our reactions toward stress are formed by our family's optimism or pessimism re: change. Bonnie grew up in a home where change was always negative. Her family environment was one of waiting for doomsday. When they moved it was not to a better house (altho it was) but it was attributed to financial pressures. She was always reminded of the dangers and hostility of the outside world and discouraged from leaving the safety of home, even when she wanted to go away to college. Mike, on the other hand, grew up with a lot of freedom (often more the privilege of boys than girls) and learned to enjoy the competition of team sports. Activity rather than thought and analysis has always been his "modus operandi." Mike looks forward to change as positive.

TYPES OF STRESS
PHYSIOLOGICAL STRESS

From a physiological perspective, a change in bodily functioning, such as that which occurs during illness, sets up a stress reaction. Conversely, it is also widely recognized that many diseases are instigated by stress.

Does stress express itself as physiological symptoms for you or is it time for you to have a check up and determine whether you have a physical problem that is creating the stress symptoms? Take the following test below and indicate which of these problems are yours. Check those which are a frequent problem for you in the last three months and then consider whether this may be a response to stress or is it time to see a doctor.

1. Irritability_____
2. Loss of appetite_____
3. Trouble sleeping_____
4. Headaches_____
5. Tired feeling_____
6. Overeating_____
7. Ringing in ears_____
8. Lump in throat_____
9. Dry mouth_____
10. Racing heart beat_____
11. Skin rashes_____
12. Stomach pains_____
13. High blood pressure_____
14. Nightmares_____
15. Allergy problems_____
16. Lower back pain_____
17. Muscle aches/pains_____
18. Indigestion_____
19. Hives_____
20. Menstrual distress_____
21. Muscle twitching_____
22. Frequent forgetting_____
23. Heavy drinking_____
24. Use of nonprescription drugs_____
25. Asthma attack_____
26. Nausea or vomiting_____
27. Depression_____
28. Minor accidents_____
29. Cold hands or feet_____
30. Sexual problems_____
31. Feelings of anger_____
32. Constipation_____
33. Nervousness_____
34. Heavy smoking_____
35. Hyperventilation_____
36. Infections_____
37. Peptic ulcer_____
38. Dermatitis_____
39. Colitis attack_____
40. Diarrhea_____

Physiological stress requires "destressing your body." This is achieved through rest, relaxation, exercise and nutrition. Exercise provides a tension release and often serves the additional purpose of taking our mind off the very problems that are causing us to create "Distress" and therefore serves a double purpose.

However, nutrition is becoming increasingly recognized as a cause or effect of stress requiring support and an increase attention during periods of stress.

The need for nutritional support during periods of stress is becoming much more evident. Increased tissue requirements for vitamins can occur under a variety of conditions so that nutritional deficiencies may develop on diets that had previously been adequate. For example, various stress factors such as pregnancy, lactation, smoking, alcohol, severe injury, various illnesses such as infections, and certain drugs can increase nutritional demands. Combinations of various stress factors, which by themselves can be only mildly stressful, may lead to severe nutritional demands.

Inadequate ingestion of vitamins may occur from a diet of inferior quality or from *failure to ingest an adequate diet* through ignorance, poor eating habits, or *emotional or physical illness*. Under any of these circumstances, a physician may elect to recommend a dietary supplement.

Certain individuals are exposed to deficient intakes of vitamins as a result of eccentric diets, such as food faddism, and the avoidance of food because of anorexia. Intakes of vitamins less than those recommended can also occur in subjects on reducing diets and among the elderly people who eat little food for economic or social reasons. The consumption of excessive amounts of alcohol can also lead to inadequate intakes of vitamins and other nutrients.

Increased tissue requirements for vitamins may cause a nutritional deficiency to develop despite the ingestion of a diet that had previously been adequate. There is good evidence that requirement for some vitamins increase during stress.

The ability of a patient to recover from an illness, injury or operation is closely related to his previous and current nutrient supply. Rare indeed is the patient who cannot be aided by proper nutritional guidance, since *nutrition is probably the most important environmental factor affecting health and disease*.

The Recommended Dietary Allowances (RDA) are designed to serve as goals for planning food supplies rather than for planning diets for sick or injured patients. Although they provide a buffer against increased needs during common stresses, they are not necessarily adequate to meet the additional requirements of persons depleted by disease, traumatic stresses, or prior dietary inadequacies.

Since a deficiency of nutrients in body tissues can be caused by gastrointestinal handicaps and metabolic abnormalities as well as by dietary deficiencies, it is evident that physical stresses of many types can cause or contribute to malnutrition.

In major illness, marked metabolic alternations may be produced by physiological and psychological stresses; losses of nutrients from the body may be unduly large, and intake may be poor. This will produce rapid nutritional deficiency which will be especially severe if there were pre-existing depletions. It is far more difficult to correct nutritional deficiency than to prevent it.

EMOTIONAL STRESS

As we have already said stress is a response to change and as you will see in the life change test all emotions can then be considered as stimulants of stress. This includes love as well as hate and depression as well as elation. However, once again, it is the response to these emotions that determines if the stress works for you or against you. Amongst those emotions that are most destructive is worry.

We all know people like Linda, who greets any change with worry. Linda suffers from the "what if syndrome." Whether it is joy that has come into her life or unhappiness or a new event or the possibility of change, Linda's reaction always is "what if something goes wrong?" Before she was chosen for her new job, she, of course, was very anxious in the weeks preceding her selection (contributing to tremendous negative stress). She was now worried about "what if I can't do the job well" and "what if they've made a mistake." Hearing this we may laugh but we all know people who plague every aspect of their lives by anticipating every thing that can go wrong, which of course usually doesn't. One anecdote to the "what if syndrome" is "what's the worst possible thing that could happen". Try asking yourself this after you say, "what if I get the job and then I can't do the work". Obviously, the worst possible thing that can happen is that you will lose the job, which of course you would not have had if they hadn't selected you in the first place. So, if you really think about it, you are really back where you started except that you have created tremendous negative stress for yourself by anticipating all the terrible reprecussions. This attitude, astonishingly enough, even carries over to love, which can easily lead (in a worrier) to the worry that this person loves me now but suppose they fall out of love with me. People like Linda, who turns her emotions into negative stress, miss the joy of life and do not stave off the disappointments because, as we should know by now, worrying does nothing to change anything unless we act upon our real concerns.

In addition to physiological signs of negative stress, there are psychological signs of stress. Go down the following list and see if you have experienced for periods of time any of these disorders. These are changes in personality that often signal underlying stress and if recognized in time you can stop and act upon the cause of the stress before these symptoms result in a serious disorder.

PSYCHOLOGICAL SIGNS OF DISTRESS

Hypochondria

Insomnia

Missing appointments or deadlines

Sudden propensity for mistakes

Confusing or forgetting dates, places, times, or other details

Making safe choices, but not necessarily the best choices

Sexual or romantic indiscretions

Sudden increase in drinking or smoking habits

Excessive worrying, especially over trivial matters

Excessive or irrational mistrust of associates

Constant harping on personal failures or shortcomings

Constant reference to death or suicide
Prolonged periods of brooding
Sudden reversals of usual behavior

It might seem that the solution to stress is to eliminate stress from our lives. However, since this would mean eliminating all change as well as all responsibility, goals and motivation, in itself it would set up another stress and, that is, the stress of lethargy, loneliness and ennui, which in itself is stressful. Therefore, it really seems that the only resolution is to find ways to deal positively with stress.

Work can be a source of great "Eustress" and great "Distress." Responsibility, achievement and success give us good feelings about ourselves and strengthen our ability to deal with other situations. For many, work is the single most important function of their lives. Of course, we all know the risk of the "workaholic" that uses work to create "Distress" rather than picking from it what is positive. Here, too, the worrier can easily turn work into "Distress" by worrying, of course, about their performance in spite of reassurance or, in fact, feeling guilty about success.

Much has been written about the "Type A Personality." This is often the workaholic. Take the following test and see what your inclinations are:

"TYPE A" PROFILE

_____ Speak the last few words of your sentence rapidly.
_____ Always move, walk, and eat rapidly.
_____ Feel impatient with rate at which most events take place.

77

_____ Usually attempt to finish others' sentences.

_____ Become unduly irritated when traffic is slow.

_____ Find it intolerable to watch others do tasks you could do faster.

_____ Usually look for summaries of interesting literature.

_____ Indulge in polyphasic thought, trying to think of or do two or more things simultaneously.

_____ Ponder business problems while away from the office.

_____ Pretend to listen to others but remain preoccupied with your own thoughts.

_____ Almost always feel vaguely guilty when you relax.

_____ Don't take time to appreciate surroundings, i.e., sunsets, scenic beauty, etc.

_____ Attempt to schedule more and more in less and less time.

_____ Possess a chronic sense of time urgency.

_____ Feel compelled to challenge another like yourself.

_____ Recognize aggressive behavior in yourself which may not be noticed by others.

_____ Frequently clench fist in conversation.

_____ Bang your hand upon a table or pound one fist into palm of other in order to emphasize a point.

_____ Habitually clench your jaw or grind your teeth.

_____ Believe your success has been due to your ability to get things done faster than others.

_____ Evaluate your own and others' activities in terms of numbers.

_____ Total

Key: Total the number of checks made above. If there are seven or fewer, there is little likelihood you are a Type A personality; seven to twelve checks indicate a tendency toward a "Type A" personality structure, while more than twelve suggest you are a "Type A" personality.

Becoming aware of your attitudes and behaviors that are causing negative stress can help you determine what you can change and how you can reduce your stress.

COPING WITH STRESS: GOING FOR EUSTRESS INSTEAD OF DISTRESS

1. *ABILITY TO ADAPT*

Adapting involves beginning with a realistic assessment of your situation. Is there corrective action that you can take? In the case of Bonnie and Mike, Mike has assumed that the corrective action is to continue working as hard as he can and to accept the situation. This involves the second adaptive approach which is acceptance. When you are in a situation, such as a traffic jam or confronted by an angry boss or spouse and you cannot change it at that moment, accepting it reduces the stress that we place on our body in that situation. At some later point, you can re-evaluate it to determine whether there is corrective action you can take or whether you just have to learn to let it go.

*Adapted from Friedman, Meyer and Rosenman, Ray H., Type A Behavior and Your Heart. New York: Fawcett Crest, 1974.

Learning to let go is an important factor in minimizing your distress.

Another aspect is to refuse to engage in "if only" or "it's not fair" attitudes. If you can't change the situation, you are only going to aggravate yourself by dwelling on what you would like to be that is not.

2. *MAINTAIN A REGULAR REGIMEN IN THE FACE OF DISTRESS*

This helps to maintain a sense of yourself in the face of change and also encourages keeping change to a minimum when you are in a period of distress.

3. *SOCIAL SUPPORT*

At a time like this Bonnie could use social support. Friends might help her see the reality of the situation she is in and also help her overcome her conflicts about competition. Stress is often a time of loneliness as well. Feeling alone creates distress; feeling that you have support even though you have to handle this alone helps overcome the negative feelings.

4. *AVOID ADVERSE BEHAVIORS*

Although the temptation is great to escape the stress through smoking, drugs, drinking, overeating or other acting-out behavior, these behaviors in themselves are not only dangerous to health but also intensify the stress because ultimately suppression creates strain, ages the body and leaves us with the original stress not only avoided but now exacerbated.

5. *TRY TO IDENTIFY THE CAUSE OF DISTRESS*

Anger, psychological withdrawal and self-destructive behavior may be an automatic stress release response but they do not identify the real feelings or the cause of emotional stress. Until these are identified, you cannot begin to take corrective action to quell the anxiety.

Lastly, it helps to know that not only are you not alone but that your reaction is "normal and appropriate." Below is the Life Change Unit Rating Scale which has been devised to indicate stress levels of various changes that occur in our lives and can be expected to affect us. The higher the number of Life Change Units the more stress it has been determined that this change is accompanied by. Indicate which changes you have experienced in the past year and knowing where your stress inventory falls adjust the rest of your life to compensate or overcome these other pressures.

LIFE CHANGE UNIT RATING

Enter your total points beside each change in the column category "Yours" for any of these changes that have occurred in your life in the past year. Total the "Yours" column for a grand total of your own Life Change Unit Rating.

Work Events	Life Change Units	Yours
Fired from work	47	————
Retired	45	————
Major business adjustment	39	————

81

Work Events	Life Change Units	Yours
Change to different line of work	36	_____
Change in responsibilities at work	29	_____
Trouble with boss	23	_____
Change in work hours or conditions	20	_____

Personal

	Life Change Units	Yours
Major personal injury or illness	53	
Outstanding personal achievement	28	_____
Change in recreation	19	_____
Revision of personal habits	24	_____
Change in church activities	19	_____
Change in sleeping habits	16	_____
Change in eating habits	15	_____
Vacation	13	_____
Christmas	12	_____

Financial

	Life Change Units	Yours
Change in financial state	38	_____
Mortgage or loan for major purchase (home, etc.)	31	_____
Foreclosure of mortgage or loan	30	_____
Mortgage or loan for lesser purchase (car, TV, etc.)	17	_____

Family

Death of a spouse	100	————
Divorce	73	————
Marital separation	65	————
Death of a close family member	63	————
Marriage	50	————
Marital reconciliation	45	————
Change in health of family member	44	————
Pregnancy	40	————
Gain of a new family member	39	————
Change in number of arguments with spouse	35	————
Son or daughter leaving home	29	————
Troubles with in-laws	29	————
Spouse starting or ending work	26	————
Change in number of family get-togethers	15	————

Social

Jail term	63	————
Sex difficulties	39	————
Death of a close friend	37	————
Start or end of formal schooling	26	————
Major change in living conditions	25	————
Changing to a new school	20	————
Change in residence	20	————
Change in social activities	18	————
Minor violations of the law	11	————
	Total	————

*Holmes, T.H. and Rahe, R.H. "The Social Readjustment Rating Scale," Journal of Psychosomatic Research. (1967) 11:213-218.

The following scale indicating the potential for good health based on the number of significant changes in your life within one year:

Less than 150 points	Good
151-300 points	Fair
More than 300 points	Poor

Of course, change cannot be avoided—life is a series of constant changes. Ask then, not, "How can I avoid change?"—but rather, "How can I cope with change and make it work for me?"

SUMMARY

Stress is a response to change. As a healthy response, stress arouses us to act. We can allow it to have a positive or negative effect on us. How we react to the vagaries of life determines whether we behave with increased energy and dynamism or stumble about, sapped of strength. Developing psychological and physical source strategies effects this difference.

CHAPTER VI

HOW TO FEEL GOOD BY LOOKING AND FEELING BETTER

A healthy mind leads to a healthy body and the reverse also is true—a healthy body is necessary for a healthy mind. The person who looks good, feels healthy, eats well and exercises with wisdom and discipline, tells the world: "I think I'm special—I care about myself enough to keep myself in top shape. So much self-respect can't be unwarranted: You should respect me too."

You cannot feel good if you are tired, sluggish, overweight and undernourished. One of the essentials of looking and feeling good is good nutrition. In one sense, the body is a complex machine capable of performing many functions and it is in need of special fuels and constant maintenance.

Barring severe and sudden illness or accident, the way we age reflects the way we are in the habit of living. The person with the straight back, raised rib cage and healthy energetic stride is not too likely to be immobile when older. The foundation of good health— for young and old—is good diet.

NUTRITION

Fortunately, nature provides a vast array of nutrients to keep our minds and bodies thriving. The basic ones are proteins, carbohydrates, fats and oils, vitamins, minerals, enzymes and liquids. (The body is from 50% to 75% water, a percentage that must be maintained. Yet too many of us drink too little water).

PROTEIN

Proteins are considered the "building blocks of life," and provide the essentials for muscles, blood, skin, hair, nails and the internal organs (including the brain). Too little protein can cause big problems. So can too much. Balance is the key to feeling good. Certainly a balanced diet (one that includes the four basic food groups—whole grains/cereals, dairy products, green and yellow vegetables, fresh fruits, fish, fowl and some meat) increases your chances at living a balanced life. Too much protein not only becomes unwanted fat, it can contribute to other disorders. Too much meat protein, for example, has been blamed for high uric acid counts, gout, irritated mucous linings of the bladder, urethra and sexual organs, arthritis and other difficulties, including the ingestion of residual antibiotics and hormones fed to grazing animals to keep them both healthy and profitable for the breeders and butchers. NONMEAT PROTEINS are in plentiful supply. They include eggs, milk, cheese and other fish, fowl, and animal products. Non-animal sources of protein include nuts and whole-grain products.

CARBOHYDRATES

Vegetables, fruits and breads—are transformed by the body into glycogen, the chief fuel of the brain which is stored in the liver and the muscles. Without enough glycogen, the body goes into ketosis, an emergency state. Since the liver can store limited amounts of glycogen (the rest of the sugar not stored as glycogen becomes fat), the supply must be added to constantly. Glycogen, the body's primary fuel, must supply energy to the brain daily. If the glycogen supply runs low, the body must fuel itself with stored fats. Without enough carbohydrates on hand, the body can't burn the fats thoroughly. As a result, partly burned fats accumulate and these are called ketone bodies. Ketone bodies are always present in small amounts but when they start building up, ketosis results. Symptoms include a demand for water from body cells and frequent urination. Allowed to continue, it can prove life-threatening, with coma one of its symptoms.

Carbohydrates (carbon, oxygen and hydrogen compounds—the sugars and starches consumed by humans) are a source of energy. Sugar, a carbohydrate component, is one of our energy sources. Since it abounds in fruits, vegetables, milk and wholegrain products, we are bound to take in too much sugar if we reguarly consume sweet snacks and beverages too. Too much sugar can, ironically, result in a lack of energy— fatigue and irritability. Why? Because too much sugar overstimulates the body's insulin production. This, in turn, causes too much sugar to be withdrawn from the body by the liver and the muscles (some of it for storage as fat). What begins as a large intake of sugar into the bloodstream ends up as a low-blood-sugar level.

FATS AND OILS

Again, nature demands that a balance be observed. Cutting out all fats and oils completely can cause trouble. For one thing, they are an important source of energy; they also insulate body organs. Fats and oils are found in animals, fish and fowl and in their products, as well as in plants. Composed mostly of fatty acids, fats come in many forms, including saturated, unsaturated and polyunsaturated, as anyone who has heard TV commercials can tell you. Saturated fats harden at room temperature—notice the layer of fat that hardens on your dinner plate after a meat meal. Almost invariably, the unsaturated fats are liquid in form at room temperature and are derived from vegetable products. Saturated fats are the most strongly linked with cholesterol.

CHOLESTEROL

Regarded as an arch villain by many—cholesterol is essential to good health in *balanced* amounts. Cholesterol aids in the production of adrenal and sex hormones, bile salts and vitamin D. Lacking sufficient supply, the body will produce cholesterol on its own in certain amounts. Too much cholesterol in the circulatory system—and this varies from individual to individual—can result in the formation of cholesterol deposits in the linings of blood vessels, gradually clogging them. If a major artery is clogged completely, a heart attack results. Some doctors maintain that problems arise not from cholesterol so much as from the body's inability to handle cholesterol properly—because of insufficient lecithin.

LECITHIN is an emulsifier of fat. It causes cholesterol to break down into small particles that can be carried away, thus preventing large chunks from collecting in vessel linings. Doctors who maintain this view say modern food processing has destroyed large portions of the lecithin that foods normally would provide. Vegetable oils, for instance, if not processed (hydrogenated, for example) are a source of lecithin.

All components of nutrition are closely interrelated. Just as lecithin helps process cholesterol, and just as carbohydrates are converted by the body into glycogen or fats, so, too, do vitamins, minerals and enzymes help the body to use and store foods. The B vitamins, for example, are of major importance. So are such nutrients as magnesium, potassium and phosphorous. A balance of vitamins, minerals and trace elements are essential to good health. Here is a brief list of some vitamins and their functions.

VITAMIN A: Fat soluble, stored in liver; essential for growth and maintenance of cells of skin, lining of eyes and lungs; helps resist infection, aids night vision. *Sources:* Animal livers, green vegetables, milk, eggs, butter, most cheeses.

B-GROUP VITAMINS: Water soluble. Include B_1 (thiamine) B_2 (riboflavin), niacin, B_6, folic acid and B_{12}. They promote growth, metabolism of body cells, blood cells; necessary for sex hormone production. B_2 (riboflavin) contributes to growth, metabolism of all cells of the body. Niacin—aids growth, intestinal functions and sugar metabolism. B_6—protein metabolism, cell functions. Folic acid—aids in proper formation of red blood cells. B_{12}—aids in fat and sugar metabolism, blood formation, growth.

SOURCES OF B VITAMINS: Whole-grain products, wheat germ, liver, green leafy vegetables, milk, molasses, peanuts, dried peas, beans.

VITAMIN C (ascorbic acid)—water soluble. Essential for healthy blood vessels, blood clotting, healing of wounds, healthy connective tissue, iron absorption, strong teeth and bones. *Sources:* Citrus fruits, green leafy vegetables, tomatoes, potatoes, cantaloupe, strawberries, bean sprouts. (There has been debate for years over whether or not vitamin C helps prevent the common cold. Nobel Prize winner Linus Pauling, among others, contends that it does.)

VITAMIN D—Fat soluble; needed for healthy bones, teeth, proper metabolism of calcium and phosphorous. *Sources:* Sunlight, milk, fish, liver, butter, eggs.

VITAMIN E—Fat soluble; aids proper functioning of heart and bloodstream, sexual glands, muscles, joints. *Sources:* Unrefined, cold-pressed vegetable oils, especially wheat germ oil and soybean oil; wheat germ, spinach, brown rice.

MINERALS are also important to good health, including CALCIUM, sometimes called "nature's tranquilizer." Calcium, found primarily in bones and teeth, also is found in the soft tissue cushioning the nerve endings. Too little calcium results in nervousness, irritability. Calcium helps promote healthy blood clotting, healthy muscles, absorption of iron. *Sources:* Milk, cheese, yogurt, raw vegetables, egg yolk, sesame seeds, oats, nuts, brown rice, wheat germ.

Other important minerals include phosphorous, iron, potassium, sodium (salt-limited amounts) chlorine, magnesium, sulfur, silicon, fluorine, and zinc.

ENZYMES—An enzyme is a substance produced by living tissue. It stimulates specific chemical changes and it is, therefore, a catalyst. Certain enzymes are produced in the body. Others must come from the food we eat. Enzymes are essential to survival—they transform the food we eat into the living cells of our body. They help increase resistance to disease and help speed the healing process. They affect hormone secretion. Enzymes are destroyed in foods by cooking and processing. *Sources: Raw* vegetables, raw fruits, nuts and seeds.

The consumption of such raw foods also supplies roughage, (or fiber) or cellulose, which helps the body eliminate waste and utilize fuel sufficiently.

Try to stay as natural and balanced as possible in your diet—cook fresh foods whenever possible. Read labels. Avoid those with sugar and salt added or those in which sugar and salt figure at or near the top of the list. Remember that -ose endings on ingredients indicate sugar. A label may not say "sugar" but instead my list fructose, maltose, dextrose, lactose, or sucrose. These are all sugars. The most fattening thing you can eat is fat. But to eat no fat also will cause problems eventually.

EXERCISE—Food is fuel for a complex machine in need of energy. And the energy needs to be expended. If you are what you eat, you also are what you do (or don't) do.

The body is comprised of many movable parts and far too often, far too many of them don't move as frequently as their original design seems to have intended. People who haven't entered the world of steady exercise for fitness and pleasure often suppress a sneer and a small shriek of fear when in the presence of those who have.

"Gym?" says the overweight woman with a laugh. "For me the only function that word serves is in being a man's first name." She hopes the witticism will evoke a laugh and deflect attention away from her figure.

Exercise is something the physically fit miss when they do without it and something that those who aren't physically fit try to miss at every opportunity.

Like children who aren't impressed when hearing "vegetables are good for you," many of us will reject exercise as an option—until we are ordered to pursue it as a survival mechanism.

Don't wait for a doctor's orders to exercise. Don't link it with grim survival, either, but with feeling good. If exercise is good for you it can also be fun. There are all kinds—stretching, isometrics, aerobics, swimming, bicycling, tennis, volleyball, other team sports, jogging—to name a few.

You do not have to run the New York City Marathon to participate in healthy exercise. In fact, you do not have to run at all. All you have to do is get out of your car—and start walking.

Walking is the best exercise of all. A *brisk* walk is one of the best exercises in the world. There are many ways to walk but walking with a purpose is the best way. It helps you to build up your endurance, to step up your metabolism, to *get somewhere* under your own steam. And it gets you away from sedentary routines, out into the world among sights, sounds, creatures and people. It is at first a challenge and eventually becomes a pleasure.

Walking will improve your circulation and thus lower blood pressure, serum cholesterol and triglycerides levels; it will improve the complexion and help make more flexible the skin, muscles, bones and ligaments. Walking helps your body burn off impurities, increases the oxygen in your blood and surprisingly enough, combats fatigue.

But walking, while basic, is just one of many forms of exercise. There are many others.

Judy wakes up at 5:30 every morning and, tunes in to an exercise TV show, just to feel "fully awake," she says. Exercising in tandem with attractive people and copying their movements on the screen insures her accuracy in exercising and keeps her striving to keep up with them.

Ellen gets up at 6:30 and watches the news on TV while pedaling five miles on her stationary exercise bike. By 7 a.m., she says, she is "wide awake," revved up and ready to start the day.

Tom goes to the gym for an hour every evening after work. The exercise he does there gives him, he says, "a second wind" with which to enjoy the rest of the evening. Previously, he likes to recount, he'd get home, eat a dull meal and fall asleep watching the 7 p.m. news.

Ken works in the city, lives in the suburbs. Three mornings a week he arrives in town early to play tennis with friends before going to the office.

Chuck lives in Manhattan not far from the East River. Summer and winter, neighbors are accustomed to seeing a canoe moving down the street (propelled by Chuck's legs) toward the river at least four evenings a week. He says it "makes my day."

Kitty does housekeeping daily and does it in such a manner—bending, stretching, reaching—that it gives her healthy exercise all day long.

Paul (he's 30) goes rollerskating four nights a week and loves it.

Dancing, swimming, jogging, weightlifting, yoga, sports are ways of maintaining a healthy physique. Through exercise, not only do you maintain a healthy body and good blood circulation, but you maintain emotional well-being as well. A sense of well-being and of feeling "up" are the direct result of chemical changes. You wind up feeling "high" after a workout and experience an "all's right with the world" feeling long after you've completed the workout. Exercise beats drugs for feeling good. And it makes you look good too.

LOOKING BETTER

Everybody always thinks they can look better. Having seen your face and body in the mirror year after year, you probably have a detailed idea of how you actually look and how you'd like to look—what you would like to change about your looks.

Take another look at yourself. Examine every square inch of you—sans makeup, sans clothing—in the privacy of your room before a mirror. Be sure the lighting is good. Now, make a list of everything—we mean everything—you would like to change about your physical being. Work from head to toe, or in order of your priorities.

When you have completed your list, review it. Go back over it and, next to each item on the list, describe what you would have to do to achieve the change you'd like to make. And almost anything can be changed or modified.

For example, you can't BE taller, but you can LOOK taller by wearing "tall" clothing (solid colors, stripes, heels on shoes that add to the appearance of height, even hairstyles and good posture—standing taller—can make a person appear to be taller than actual height.

When Denise was told how beautiful she was, she laughed.

"I did it myself," she said. "Four years ago, at the age of 21, I decided I wanted to go through life beautiful. So I redid everything—but everything.

I had my ears pinned back, my nose bobbed, my chin extended and lightly cleft. I wore braces for a year, got tinted contact lenses, straightened my hair, lost 20 pounds and gained a breast implant. I feel great and it was worth every penny that I had to borrow.

What courage!

Look at your list and decide what really bothers you enough to change it. Start planning right now how you will go about effecting that change.

If you don't care enough about something you consider an imperfection to change it, accept it and determine to feel good about the way you are—the way you have decided to be.

ARE YOU HAVING ANY FUN?

All of life should not—must not—be grim and earnest. Put a little grin in with the grim. Give yourself room for some play and relaxation, too. All your efforts—healthy diet, healthy exercise—will be for naught if you make your approach strictly work. Pleasure and relaxation must accompany the health process. You can't feel good without doing things you feel good about doing.

Vacations are important. They change the routine, change your way of looking at the world, give you a new set of challenges and pleasures, a sense of adventure. But vacations, for most of us, occur only once a year. If you can't go off on a cruise or an expedition to Europe or a safari to Africa, you can give yourself little parcels

96

of time for pleasure and relaxation—a small chance to "get away from it all." This might mean relaxing with a drink or a glass of soda water after work, chatting with friends, it might mean a nap, or meditation, or exercising. It can mean almost anything your schedule and preferences require, but it is important to intersperse work with periods of relaxation. Once again, balance is the key to a feel-good way of life.

Joyce and Arthur leave the work week behind them every Friday evening. They go off to their country house and take a complete break from the city. They spend their weekend doing things they don't do during the week—reading, napping, gardening, preparing meals for long hours together in the kitchen and having company occasionally. Newlyweds, they enjoy their privacy, enjoy an interest in antiques and sometimes shop at a local flea market.

On the other hand, there's George.

George finds brief interludes—such as weekends—disruptive. He has set up his schedule to work for three weeks straight after which he takes off one week every month vacationing out of town either alone or with friends who allow him to visit.

Sheila and Stan have another idea.

The parents of young children, they must budget their money carefully and can't afford to spend the money on vacations and feel uneasy about leaving their youngsters with sitters too often. But they have worked out an amenable arrangement. One night a week they hire a babysitter and go out with friends. Once a month, they spend a night at a hotel in town and leave the kids with either set of grandparents. They will leave the children with alternate grandparents to spend the night once a month—while Shiela and Stan steal quietly back home to honeymoon alone together.

Bodies and minds seem to mature and get into ruts. Perhaps it's efficient to pre-program ourselves, but we pay the price for such efficiency in living humdrum existences that aren't challenging or fun or pleasurable.

If you want to feel good and look good you've got to be flexible and you've got to establish goals for yourself. Maybe the challenge of conquering new worlds might be more than you'd care to take on, but conquering new satisfactions in the world you're already occupying can afford you new adventures, new satisfactions that should keep you going efficiently and happily well into oldest old age.

SUMMARY:

Exercise and diet and psychological fitness go hand in hand. A sense of balance—goal-setting and work and discipline—are wonderful. They help build your confidence because you learn by doing that you can accomplish what you set out to do. And that builds up your sense of self-esteem.

Don't be entirely grim about the process, however. Take in the fun of successfully shaping your life to be as you wish it to be, your body to look as you want it to. And, have fun doing it. Vacations, time for family, friends, time for pleasure—these are essential to well-being. Enjoy yourself, your life.

The sound body/sound mind state requires knowledge of your particular body and what works well for it. A sensible program of good nutrition, exercise and pleasurable activities as well as work, will certainly have you—and others—thinking of you as a person who looks and feels good.

CHAPTER VII

HOW TO FEEL GOOD BY LIVING AN ORGANIZED LIFE

If you want to be certain a job will get
done, assign it to a busy person.

"How do you manage to accomplish so much?"
Those of us who have not actually asked that question of a super-achiever certainly have pondered it silently. Generally, when such *wundervolk* are asked such a question they say something like, "I push myself and pare the nonessentials from my schedule." or: "I get up earlier and try to keep distractions to a minimum."

What they are saying is they make a *concerted effort to achieve* what they *set out* to do—they are *committed to a goal* and to a *plan* that will help them reach it—*and* they *set priorities*. In short, they are organized.

HOW TO GET ORGANIZED

Knowing what you want to accomplish is the first step. Outlining how to get it done, in manageable segments, is the second. Taking the first step—starting the work—then becomes the logical next move, rather than one you might take, someday, when everything gets clearer in your mind about the project you want to tackle.

It took a pleasant time after work one night to help Shirley clarify what she wanted.

> Shirley and some of her co-workers stopped at a local pub one night after work and really hit it off. She hated to see the fun end and was tempted to invite them over to her apartment—she lived nearby—for a potluck dinner and more conversation. All were her age—in their mid 20's—single, and full of witticisms and high spirits.

> She did not yield to the temptation, however, Shirley could hardly invite anyone in to see her place. It was such a mess, she scarcely liked to have to look at it herself.

> Shirley hadn't dusted or vacuumed in weeks; most of the clothing she had worn in the last few days was draped on doorknobs or over chairs; her shoes were in a heap near the front door; newspapers, read and unread, cluttered the floor at one end of the sofa. Towels, makeup and assorted lingerie, washed and unwashed, littered the bathroom; her bed was unmade; stacks of magazines and unsorted mail covered table tops. Dishes to be put away graced the kitchen countertops and a pot and some glasses (all filled with water) were sitting in the sink. Both her windows and her curtains needed washing and the formerly white

101

slats of window blinds were practically gray—each one coated with dust and city soot. Her laundry hamper was so full it wouldn't close and there were three shopping bags full of returnable soda pop bottles waiting to be taken to the market. People who had known Shirley since her early childhood never could understand her housekeeping (or lack of it); her mother was extremely orderly. Shirley had grown up in a well-run household.

Perhaps that, precisely, was the reason for the "mess up" in Shirley's life. She had resisted Mom's militant neatness and scheduling at home and was still resisting it now—in her own home. Instead of leaving home, then, Shirley had brought home, and Mom, along with her to a new address. No wonder it was so very crowded and unwieldy where Shirley lived. She hadn't made room for herself!

Once all this began to dawn on Shirley, she began to face the idea that life in her apartment wasn't doing much to promote her ease or enjoyment. Instead, it was prolonging an unpleasant childhood situation that existed only in her memory. She decided to clean up her act—and her apartment—not because she "should," as Mom had said so many times, but because she wanted to live more pleasantly.

Shirley wanted to be able to open a drawer and find gloves there—in pairs—when she needed gloves. She wanted to be able to open a file folder and pull out her IRS related material when she needed to file her tax return—early for a change or, at least, on time rather than midnight on April 15. She wanted to be able to answer the door's buzzer and say with genuine delight: "Oh! Hi! Come on in for a visit. What a nice surprise."

Finally, Shirley decided to take action. In a fit of resolve, she washed and scrubbed and tossed out newspapers and did all the laundry, washed the windows and curtains, and straightened up the place so that, to the visitor who might enter, the apartment would seem a pleasant enough place to rest and talk a while. Shirley smiled to herself as she surveyed the overall effect of her labors. She asked people in to visit all weekend.

But by Thursday, the doorknobs once again were covered with clothing, the kitchen sink again was full of soaking glasses and pots and the bathroom looked like closing time after a department store lingerie sale. Clearly, transforming the apartment into a pleasant stage-setting was possible and rewarding. But it was also temporary, cosmetic and didn't solve the basic problem making it a comfortable home. Shirley's lack of organization affected every inch of her domicile.

She went to the public library and got a few books on "How to Organize." Following their advice, she made a list in a notebook set aside just for this "organizing my home" project. She listed just a few problems she wanted to solve, such as:

1) I want my living room and bathroom to at least look presentable at all times, ready for visitors. I don't want to feel that if I let people see how it *usually* looks in here, they'll run off, convinced that I'm nuts.

2) My living room looks like a paper drive—magazines, newspapers, mail—and like a rag

shop—clothes strewn all over. I've got to control this.

3)   Until I broke down and washed the windows, I hadn't seen the sunlight for nearly a year. How do I make time for this chore on a regular basis?

4)   There were some clothes in the hamper that I'd forgotten I owned. But I don't have time to do every housekeeping chore and work all the overtime I have to work in this new job.

5)   More often than not, there are dishes in the sink—and that's almost funny, since I seldom cook. I don't cook because it's too much trouble to search for a can opener or a pancake turner and I haven't seen the eggbeater since moving day. My cupboards and my closets and my drawers seem to work like garbage disposers—I toss things into them, never to see them again.

One thing was clear *before* she started the list: Shirley wanted to get her apartment organized and she wanted to adopt a routine that would *keep* it organized. After writing the list it became even clearer how much she needed to organize in her life.

She had placed at the top of her list the goal to have her home neat enough to welcome—not scare off—visitors. She wanted her home to "look presentable at all times."

How to achieve that goal?

First, she had to examine both her use of the space she occupied and her daily routines from rising time through bedtime.

Breaking problems down into manageable segments is one way to succeed at solving them. If, like Shirley, you want your living room to "look good at all times," try to examine it with new eyes, in an effort to understand what it can do best and what it should not be asked to do at all. Look at the room from a doorway, trying to see it as a stranger would. Examine it section by section, from the middle of one wall, say to a corner. How does that area look? Neat? Off-balance? Used to best advantage? Could it be more functional than it is now? Would the dining set go better in that area than the desk does? Is this section of the room free of traffic? Could the next wall-to-corner section afford more storage space? A chest? A bookcase? Should it hold less furniture? Continue the process until each inch of the room has been surveyed and analyzed for possibilities and for problem spots.

Walk through the room. Sit or stand in every area. Review how you see it from morning till night. Take notes. Do you have to move furniture to get to the bookshelves, leading you to leave books on tables, rather than putting them back? Write that down. Perhaps a new furniture arrangement here will help.

Do you constantly drape clothing on closet doorknobs because things fall out of the closets when you open the doors? Write that down. Doubtless, the closet needs reorganization too.

Soon you will have a list of tasks to be done in the living room so long that it probably will have you throwing up your hands in defeat. Up till now, that has been the effect of so many tasks on you. But not this time. This time, you're going to make two lists. One is for tasks that must be done *NOW* (because they are creating too much discomfort in your life) and another list for tasks to be done eventually to make life pleasant. Keep your MUST list limited to a half-dozen or fewer items so you won't be tempted to give up before you've begun.

Set specific times to work on a MUST problem—and stick to those times, whether you decide to devote 10 minutes a night to them or one hour three times a week. Once you have crossed one task off your MUST list, add another, but be sure to congratulate yourself for having completed it. Ocassionally, you may perform one of the minor tasks that will make life pleasant, if not well-organized, such as washing the picture frames, polishing the now visible doorknobs or shining up the philodendron leaves. These are easy cross-offs you can accomplish while talking on the phone, perhaps. Such items are NOT to distract you from the MUST items.

And don't make your dwelling a stage-setting designed only to impress others. Shoving dishes into the refrigerator because someone else is stopping over may allow you to put up a good front, but you'll know that behind the refrigerator door lurks not merely ice cubes, but the unwashed dishes of the week.

Do your dishes not for visitors, but because *you're* worth doing dishes for. (You've got to like you before you can like others and have them like you back, remember?)

How do you handle your time? Are you getting all that you want to get from life on a daily basis? For yourself and for your loved ones? If the answer is yes, you are probably managing your time very well. Others may find that time is just seeping away, hour by hour, with long periods of little action interspersed with brief spurts of frantic panicked activity to meet a long-ignored deadline, to catch a plane for a trip arranged months ago but never really *planned* for.

Preparation and planning are distasteful to those still rebelling against the order imposed long ago by such authority figures as parents. But preparation and planning are also part of the job of life to those who aren't flailing about in primal rebellion. For example, saving for a trip abroad, reading about the history of the area you want to visit, studying the guidebooks for interesting spots of beauty or entertainment, listening to music of the region, learning a bit about the customs, the dances, the foods, the crafts, the economy, the culture, the people—leaning to speak a basic traveler's version of the language—can all be pleasurable preparatory activities that can enrich your trip and your self-confidence and widen your circle of friends as well.

Sit back, notebook in hand, and close your eyes, reviewing how you spent your time every day last week, Monday through Sunday, from rising to retiring. How does it compare with the week before? With this week, so far? Where are you losing time? Hitting snags? What *didn't* you do that could have been fun, had you planned to do it? Think about tomorrow, about the coming week. How would you like your days to differ? What would you like to accomplish? To enjoy? What people would you like to make time for?

Write in your notebook all the areas in which you waste time, run into obstacles, find yourself rushing or struggling or behind schedule. Jot down possible causes of these situations. Then write down possible solutions for them. Also design a schedule for the coming week, day by day, through the weekend. List

107

chores and obligations. (Obligations are things you must do, rather than things you chose to do, such as getting to work every day—on time—and leaving on time, taking your youngsters to Scout meetings or an elderly neighbor to the doctor's office.)

Keep your notebook for organization improvement in one spot at home and refer to it daily. Also keep an appointment book in your pocket or purse and refer to it before you go to bed each night and before you commit yourself to an appointment. Note all the things you have to do that day. In a small notebook, list such items as "pick up cleaning after work," "call the bank to find out status of account," "take Susie's purse to repair shop," etc. List these tasks in one notebook to prevent your pockets from being cluttered with dozens of sheets of paper. Crossing them off will give you a feeling of accomplishment.

Assign each task a priority rating—MUST, IMPORTANT and NOT URGENT. Business people have been making lists like this for decades—it increases their efficiency, gives them more time and a sense of well-being (even a set of reliable records). Maybe you aren't a tycoon, but you are worth a smooth-running day and, with a little effort, who knows—you might become a tycoon.

Keep another such list for your office duties, just to see how helpful this method can become. And do FIRST the tasks you hate most. It's a great feeling that the best is yet to come for the rest of the day and that the worst is over. Do the MUSTS and the IMPORTANTS first and leave the NOT URGENT items till last. If necessary, transfer these latter items over to tomorrow's TO DO list—again toward the bottom of the list. If, after three days, some items on your list aren't done, take stock of the situation. Or, could you be pretending these tasks need doing—should you just cross them off and forget it? Can you get them done easily and quickly if you make the effort? Start the next day off with new tasks, rather than three-day-old leftovers. Ask the questions, come up with answers, and make a decision that suits you and your needs.

Some things are worth doing well—but later. Some things are not worth doing at all. Still other things are not worth doing yourself.

If you have a little extra money, and precious little time to share with your mate or family or friends on weekends, but still spend Saturdays doing the laundry and housekeeping and running errands through the neighborhood, perhaps you should review your priorities and your schedule and consider buying or hiring a few conveniences for yourself.

Buy a dishwasher, hire a housekeeper to do a general weekly cleaning, perhaps even the laundry, get a teen-aged neighbor, if possible, to run errands for you on Saturday mornings.

Sondra did, finally.

Sondra works long hours as a real estate salesperson. After rushing around all day, she still feels guilty when she gets home if she doesn't straighten every room in the house and do a heavy-duty cleaning on Sunday—her only day off. She and her husband (who refuses to clean house) make good salaries and could easily afford a cleaning helper. But Sondra is trying to live up to her mother's example and Mother was an excellent housekeeper. (Mother didn't work and she also made Father relatively happy, but Sondra overlooks this.) Sondra would do well to come home, relax in a tub, chat with her husband and plan some lovely weekends for the two of them to enjoy. She is sacrificing their time to an ideal not worth fostering. Sacrifice is valuable when it contributes to your life and the lives of those around you. But Sondra's sacrificial approach to life was hurting, not helping, herself and her husband. She would be doing a far better thing if she began spending her money to gain the gift of time—and then spend that time doing things that only *she* can do, for herself, for her husband.

Organizing your life begins and ends with organizing your time to your own best advantage. And in a business economy, a favored motto is "Time is money." Planning your finances is also important.

At this very moment, could you gather the following within two minutes?

1) Your IRS forms for the last five years and all pertinent information for the coming IRS form you'll have to file?

2) All your cancelled checks and bank statements for the last five years?

3) All bills that are due—to utilities companies, charge card credit firms, bank, car loans, mortgage, taxes, rent, doctor, dentist, etc.? (As well as records of payment for these for the last two years? (And—can you cite all the payments due this month?)

4) Policies and payment records for your homeowners insurance? Apartment insurance? Car insurance?

5) Your list of valuables in a safe deposit box— and who, other than you, has a key? Your list of saving and checking accounts? List of stocks, bonds, other investments? Your will?

(If you find that No. 5 applies to you at all, even if it takes a while for you to find these things, we salute you—obviously, you have taken firm steps toward financial independence.)

Get yourself organized, for heaven's sake—it can mean the difference between profit and loss, peace of mind and a lawsuit, the ability to benefit those you wish to benefit or the potential to burden them with problems you could have avoided, through a little planning.

Just as you would survey a room, section by section, to analyze how it could function better, analyze your financial picture. Get an accordion file, or envelopes, or a filing cabinet. Or all three. Give yourself special envelopes for each of those items listed—five envelopes, if you wish, or three; whatever number that may suit your needs and your system. Except for Item No. 3, all the envelopes or folders can be filed out of sight but within easy reach. All should be kept up-to-date, with material filed in the order received (mail, receipts, new orders, addenda). Item No. 3 qualifies for a title such as "current finances" or, simply, "bills". Set aside a period of time for a particular day or days each week to review and pay your bills and file them systematically. For example, you may want to staple all credit charge slips to the appropriate credit company bill of the month and then file it with a note to refer to a cancelled check. You may want a separate file folder for each credit company, each utility, doctor, etc. You might also want to note in your datebook that you paid Company X with Check No. Y on the day you mail the payment.

Carefully kept datebooks can keep you in touch with a great deal of your life—appointments you must keep (or cancel) obligations you must meet, tasks you must accomplish, dates to look forward to, birthday and anniversary cards to send to give pleasure to others— good intentions accomplished with ease and pride. Looking back on a datebook from the previous year can be enlightening If you've never yet kept one persistently through an entire year, being able to do so will give you a sense of pride and accomplishment. Datebooks help you plan your future, live up to your present without missing important moments and even give you day-to-day accounts of your past.

If you've really committed yourself to becoming an organized person, you will see the benefits of such commitment in a well-kept datebook. You will begin to plan your present so that the future will become more accessible—and satisfying.

For fun, take a sheet of paper and square off a month full of days five years from now—you choose the month. Now, for fun, fill out each square, hour by hour, day by day, with activities you really would like to be doing in five years. Think about it carefully and fill in each day with activities you honestly would want to be pursuing.

Is your current schedule full of challenge, changes,

social and business events? Cultural pleasures or accomplishments? Volunteer work? Financially rewarding moments. Creatively satisfying hours? Travel? School? A new career? A new romance? New possessions? A new setting? A housekeeper? An accountant? Fame?

Cover that page of the future, think about it for a day, then go back to it. How much of it do you really want? How much of it can you actually get? (You can't become a prima ballerina at 38 if you've never had any training, but you *can* become active in the local ballet guild or take ballet lessons at any age.) How can you go about getting it? Starting today?

Now—today—make an entry in today's (or tomorrow's) datebook, square to launch yourself into that much-wanted picture of your life five years from now. You might start with enrollment in a dance class or a writing class. Or making an appointment with an accountant to help you organize your finances. Or hiring a woman to clean for you one day a week. Or joining a weight-reduction club, or taking language lessons or ordering a passport. Whatever it is, you'll be *planning* today for the kind of tomorrow you want enough to MAKE it happen.

Don't forget your todays. They are your most important possession. They make tomorrows rich or poverty-stricken, they make yesterdays sweet or bitter.

Get organized and start feeling good—today.

SUMMARY:

Getting organized, after years of disorganization, can, like any big change, propel you into immobility at first. Getting "into" it is the fun part.

113

But most rewarding of all, in living an organized life, is knowing that you are in charge of your life, that your keys no longer have the power to make you late for work because you can't find them, that your clothes are at your command and you won't be stuck wearing a purple shirt with green slacks because there was no other choice, that Mom's old voice and Dad's old commands are now fondly remembered instead of passively rebelled against even at this late date.

Living in a mess often means you're living in the past. Living in a mess often means you can expect more of the same tomorrow. Organizing your home, your time, your work, your life, gives you a pleasant present, a brighter future, a past that will give good memories. Organizing also gives you more free time—hours that can add up to days and months, maybe years, of enjoyable living. Could there be a better bonus?

CHAPTER VIII

HOW TO FEEL GOOD BY ENJOYING LOVE, ROMANCE & SEX

The definition of love is often attempted, rarely agreed upon. Let us say that love is an emotion, a deep affection, caring, perhaps devotion, that is the driving force behind good feelings about one's self and the goodness of life.

More than merely the feeling of "liking," love allows us intense and intimate feelings. Love. Often requiring and inspiring a passionate involvement of one's self, it provides an excitement that gives us energy and enthusiasm for life. We all need and want to experience feelings of love for someone or something. Without such feelings, our spirits waste away.

Fortunately, we can derive love experiences from a wide variety of sources—family, friends, work, learning, creativity and spiritual worship, among others.

UNDERSTANDING LOVE

If there are many forms of love, there are at least as many ways to react to them. One of the reactions love inspires is fear, and, sad to say, fear of love strikes hardest at those who most need love but are least able to accept it. Because of their timidity, they are less likely to be offered love than are more outgoing individuals.

Fear of Love

Terry is afraid of love. And she is a lonely woman. The constant criticism of her father and brothers as she was growing up left her afraid to trust anyone. Bright, witty and energetic, Terry, in her late 20's, has no trouble meeting people and attracting their interest. She is outgoing and gregarious, yet she never has been able to sustain a close love relationship with a man or friendship with a woman. She cannot believe that anyone really could love her and consequently, lets no one get close to her. Her anticipation is that anyone who gets to know her well will consequently reject her and find her inadequate, just as her father and brothers did.

Terry sees people only when she is in top form. She will cancel an appointment if she does not feel clever and "up" because she cannot risk having people experience her at less than her best. In fact, Terry will not leave her apartment if she doesn't look her best. No adult has seen Terry without her makeup on.

Even though they initially are taken by Terry, men and women alike come to feel rejected by her when she cancels appointments with them or

116

refuses their invitations. Because of her bright cheery appearance, they could never guess what really lies underneath her apparent rejection of them. (Actually, it is her fear that they will reject her!)

The only way for Terry to learn to trust is to do it—take the risk of letting people know her and accept her. That is the only way she will be able to reverse the expectation that no one will be able to find her lovable once they really get to know her. Upon hearing her story, we could see that her father and her brothers were reacting to their own conflicts about her and not to what Terry imagined were her undeniable inadequacies. But Terry will never know this until she puts herself and others to the test.

To launch her first—easy—test, Terry forced herself to go to the supermarket *without makeup*. After completing her shopping, she passed through the checkout line, spoke to people in line, to the cashier, the bagger, others and was "thrilled and stunned," she said, "because no one had run away, screaming" at the sight of her unadorned face.

This seemingly small event was monumental to Terry and went a long way toward helping her resolve her obsession about her looks. Another step forward came when she was able to answer the phone and explain, apologetically, that she didn't feel like talking at that particular moment. Wonder of wonders: Her friend *forgave* her for this!

Terry was getting to feel lots better about herself and about others. Further down the line, Terry was able to join her friends for dinner, even though she wasn't feeling pert and perky. When they asked why she wasn't her usual Life-of-the-Party self, she said, simple, that she wasn't feeling that way that evening. Surprise! Nobody asked her to leave, and she was able to join in without feeling any pressure to perform. (It is impossible to resist the urge to underline the fact that, by first liking *herself* enough to be herself, Terry was able to let *others* have a try at liking her. And she liked them enough to risk being with them even when not in top form. As a result of taking the risk, she found out that her affection for them, was reciprocated.)

Love With Strings

Ann is often very generous and a great deal of fun to be with. However, after knowing her for a while, it becomes clear that she gives only to those who can give her something in return. WE ALL KNOW OUR OWN ANNS, even though it sometimes takes a while to catch on to him or her. But in time, everybody does catch on. Many will maintain a friendship with a person like Ann because she is good company but there is no feeling of love coming from her and, consequently, none going toward her, either. Often her new acquaintances don't understand this ambivalence of feeling at first but gradually the mystery clears and they accept her for what she is—a person so filled with self-love that she really cannot love anyone not involved with her own self-interest.

Ann's self-love and motivation by self-interest is costing her dearly. For one thing, she judges others by her own standards and values. Because she thinks others are motivated solely by self-interest, she can

118

neither give nor receive love. Result: She never has an opportunity to change her perceptions of life in a dog-eat-dog world. She suspects the motives of others and keeps score constantly: I did X for A—so A owes me Y in return. Giving and spending, Ann lays waste her powers to live and love.

Those who genuinely like others feel comfortable and secure about themselves in the presence of others. As a result, they feel free to take an interest in others, share their concerns, return their affection and their love. Those like Ann, on the other hand, are so wrapped up in themselves that all their interests are self-focused and they feel unworthy and insecure. Thus, they behave as if they are powerful—generous givers of gifts and dispensers of favors. "Thank you" is a phrase they greatly enjoy *hearing* (not saying). Being so thoroughly wrapped up in themselves, and quite fearful of being vulnerable, they protect their flanks at all times. By giving, they persuade *themselves* that they are loving. By wooing others, they feel more secure; in a sense, they are buying friendship. Often, the tactics work but the underlying feelings are uncomfortable.

Giving love involves a genuine caring and respect and trust for the other person so that the reward of the relationship comes not from what is gotten but what is given.

WHEN IT COMES TO LOVE, IS IT REALLY BETTER TO GIVE THAN TO RECEIVE? The answer to that question—hard as it may be to swallow—is "YES." To put it simply: In giving, we get.

Ann, who thinks of herself as a "giving" person, feels cheated by a lack of return. If you accuse her of being self-centered, she itemizes all the things she

119

ever did for you in the last 30 years (from kindergarten onward) and she then accuses you of being selfish. At 47, Ann has never been married, has never had a long-standing love affair, in short, has had no close love relationships with men and, if the truth be known, no really satisfying, love-filled friendships with women. She doesn't understand why, but still she has an explanation. She says that because she has chosen selfish people to be friends with there is a lack of love in her life. Maybe she is right, at that. People like herself, who operate on a tit-for-tat basis, can't give and take and those *are* the people she chooses for friends.

Romance

Love and marriage may go together like a horse and carriage, as the old saw says, but they are scarcely inviolable pre-requisites for one another.

Stan, 52, has never married. But his life has been filled with love. As a salesman, he has many friends across the country. He loves his work and he loves the excitement of meeting many new and different people. He also savors the fact that *they* love *him* and look forward to his arrival in their towns. On holidays, he visits his brothers and sisters, playing Santa Claus year-round for his nieces and nephews. In the spring, he coaches a Little League baseball team and has his own weekly golf game with the "boys." When not involved with others, Stan enjoys his privacy and pursues his coin-collecting hobby, which consumes much of his time because he follows

120

out-of-town auctions and trading activities. Stan enjoys his life and values his freedom. He feels lucky to have so many feelings of love and caring in his life. He has had many long-term relationships. At his age, Stan now says he is "too young" to settle down.

Stan has experiences of many kinds of love with many people, and he calls himself lucky. But it is not a question of luck. Stan has created a full life for himself. He has intense pleasure in his hobby, his associations, his sports, and he has established many relationships that give him pleasure and satisfaction.

Because he has felt himself worthy of love and of a life worth living, he is able to give—and get—a great deal of love.

In the words of another old song, "Love is where you find it." But some people are looking in the strangest places. One of the reasons they never find their "True Love" is their attachment to the myths of the princess captive in the tower waiting to be rescued from distress by the prince on his white horse. These days most princes ride in elevators and a princess's distress may involve a flat tire on the freeway. But the core of our ideas about romance centers about that Magical Moment of accidental meeting that results not only in Love at First Sight, but happiness and fulfillment forever after.

Most of us—the romantics—firmly believe not only that this will happen, but that it is our birthright and *must* happen, spontaneously and naturally, without

121

any effort on our part. This is FANTASY ROMANCE but, sorry to note, that is what far too many of us regard as "real" romance.

While the romantics languish and resist all cures, waiting for the imagined "real" romance that never comes, cynics meet the same fate—romance never comes to them either but, they say, that's because they are "realistic." Would that they were. Actually, cynics are lambs in wolf's clothing—posing as clear-eyed, hard-headed realists but in actuality dyed-in-the-wool romantics who have given up on romance altogether, but only because they want the whole fantasy—or nothing. So, nothing's what they get.

In real life, few things truly desirable will fall in your lap or "come" to you. You have to make a little effort to get what you want.

Romance is no exception. Real romance is created, nurtured and recreated. Sure, it begins with an attraction, or "chemistry" but it is something that grows in the course of a relationship, with both partners working toward and contributing to it.

Michael has fallen in love many times, but he never manages to maintain a relationship for more than three weeks. An attractive, athletic man in his early 30's, he meets many equally attractive women. Each time, he desperately hopes this is the woman of his dreams—the perfect woman—his No. 10. For the first week, when he is pursuing her, he is convinced that, finally, this is IT. She's everything he ever wanted. However, when she starts returning his interest (usually by the second week), he begins to see her faults. What her "faults" amount to is

122

that she is merely human. But he finds it unacceptable that she has faults at all.

For one thing, her hips are too wide, for another, she laughs too loud. And she swallows peculiarly.

Poor Michael! This is the beginning of the end. By the third week, he is totally disillusioned. The romance is over. Michael expects everything to stay perfect, like his fantasy. But what he's really doing here is attempting to have romance—without love.

When love accompanies romance, each partner contributes to enriching the relationship, bringing it from infatuation into romance.

Joan and Denis understand that romance is created in your own mind and then carried out in actions. After 20 years of marriage, they enjoy each other physically and mentally as much as ever and they love each other more now than they did in the beginning.

They remember to do little romantic things for each other, perhaps by wearing a special scarf or some item of jewelry that has sentimental value for them, giving the other a small gift, or flowers, surprise birthday parties, constant praises for one another. Neither is a perfect specimen; each has gotten a bit older, a little heavier, but they see beauty in one another and they "romance" each other.

They respect the work each does toward the building of home and family and they appreciate the care and effort each puts into making the home run well and the family grow in an atmosphere of caring and sharing. They are able to enjoy a give and take with their family and with their friends. They have learned to create romance out of a long and stable love relationship.

AND WHAT ABOUT SEX?

In the words of Connie, a divorceé of 29: "We all need love, we all want romance but, sometimes, we settle for sex."

After a year of loneliness following her divorce, Connie decided it would feel good to be a woman with a man she likes and "just to have fun," she said, "even if you know this is not the person you want to spend the rest of your life with. Sex gives me a lot of pleasure and makes me feel 'up.' It gets very depressing if I don't have sexual relations with a man just because I'm waiting for a lasting love to come along."

Connie, recognizing her need for physical intimacy, was able to place sex in this perspective. In her case, this works well because she is selective of the men she dates and she really is *looking* for a lasting relationship, not just waiting for one to come along. Doing without sex, says Connie, is depressing.

"On the other hand," she adds, "I know that if I had sex with just anyone, that would depress me too. But there are some men I date of whom I can say that we are good friends and can sometimes enjoy sex together."

When sex is unrelated to feelings for the other person, when it becomes a substitute for relating, it not only becomes boring, it can also cause conflict, confusion and dissatisfaction—even a total loss of interest in relationships. That was the effect sex-for-the-sake-of-sex had on Frank.

Following his divorce last year, Frank jumped onto a merry-go-round of one-night stands and sexual conquests. After 18 years of marriage, many of them spent watching on the sidelines as his friends jumped head-first into the hey-day of the sexual revolution, Frank had been longing for his chance to join them. Free at last, he did everything he had daydreamed of doing, everything he had heard his single friends boast of having done. He bedded younger women, paid women, single and divorced women and married women—even his wife's best friend who also was newly divorced.

Frank had enough money to wine and dine women, which they still expected, despite the "revolution," and he had no trouble meeting them. But he never met anyone he wanted to stay with.

After a year, he realized he really missed the familiarity and companionship he had become accustomed to as a married man. He was hoping the "right woman" would come along but, he confessed to a buddy, the "right woman" wasn't as accessible as he had imagined. He said he was tired of the cycle of meeting, sleeping with and being bombarded by the woman's quest for an immediate relationship . . . OR her total lack of interest in one.

What Frank doesn't recognize is that his expectations are in error. He expects to find an immediately "right" relationship without having to go through the effort of getting to know someone via traditional courting. He actually never had had the experience of gradually getting to know a woman. NOT even after 18 years of marriage to his wife.

Unlike Joan and Denis, Frank and his wife didn't "court" one another. Love and sex and romance need careful nurturing. Sex is an expression of love and caring in a romantic relationship and helps couples complete their communication and express their bond of commitment. Our cultural mores have passed through phases of sexual prohibition and permission, during which women, in particular, were encouraged NOT to enjoy sexual expression and almost restrained from pursuing or initiating it (even in marriage). Despite that, many couples were able to experience physical closeness and satisfaction.

It is not surprising that Joan and Denis carry their feelings of love into sexual feelings as well. Holding and caressing when they get into bed together at night is sometimes affectionate, sometimes sexual. But the constancy of the appreciation of each other in their relationship is renewed through their physical intimacy. Even when they have argued—when there is tension between them—it is resolved before they go to sleep.

Joan has "trained" Denis to talk, rather than to sulk and, by example, she is often the first to say what is on her mind. They had little sexual experience before marriage, but they have "kept up" with the times and kept up each other's interest by reading, exploration and discussion. Their sex may not have the passion that accompanies novelty, fantasy or uncertainty, but they have the fulfillment of familiarity, intimacy and continuity from their sexual expressions of love for each other.

David and Linda should take a few notes from Joan and Denis. A young couple, married only five years, their sexual pleasure has waned with each year, rather than being renewed. They each complain to their friends that they have lost interest—that they are no longer aroused by the other—*but they do not talk to each other*.

David says he is afraid to hurt Linda's feelings by telling her that she has gained weight and he wishes she would lose it. He also would like her to wear her hair long and wishes she would wear makeup at home and turn off the TV when they got into bed. Also, he says, it would help him if she were more aggressive and let him know when *she* is interested in sex.

Linda says she doesn't want to hurt David's feelings by telling him that she doesn't like the way he makes love, that she wants to be touched differently in different places and wants more

127

affection and demonstration outside of bed, she would feel more turned on to him when she gets into bed. (But Linda hasn't told David this!)

She also says she knows that she has gained weight—she eats when she is unhappy and feels unloved.

David and Linda still feel love for one another—although chances are, without communicating, it may not be for long—but they have not taken the responsibility for guiding their relationship and for making it work. They share the erroneous belief that "it's" supposed to happen between them. But "it" doesn't just "happen." Communication is the basic ingredient for good relationships and good sex.

SUMMARY:

Love is something you have to give to get. It is not a fantasy that shines in full magic light at some magic moment when the prince meets his princess and they ride off together and live happily ever after. Love is not a product of magic, it is a source of pleasure and fulfillment that can't flourish without nurturing and commitment.

Love and be found in a variety of relationships and it is in need of constant attention. "It" doesn't just "happen." And it lasts for as long as you and those you love keep working to make it last. Communicating your feelings through loving thoughts, words and actions, whether they are pleasant feelings or not can keep romance satisfying and enriched for years, for a life-time, because it constitutes sharing on an intimate plane what matters most to the two of you.

Don't wait for your prince to come, don't keep scanning towers for your princess—your Dream Person may be on the next bus—or on the pillow next to yours, right now.

CHAPTER IX

HOW TO BE A HAPPY PERSON
AFTER YOUR DREAMS COME TRUE

"Success is a journey, not a destination"
                                —a Zen tenet.

"When you wish upon a star,
your dreams come true."

Did you ever wonder what you'd do with your life if your dreams actually did come true and you actually did achieve your goals? Often, people—once they have achieved much or all of what they set out to achieve—are amazed to find that attaining the wished-for isn't the end of the story; it's more like the beginning—and a challenging beginning at that. Such beginnings have left a number of achievers confessing to feeling "strangely uneasy" or "trapped and helpless" or "surprised" at this turn of events.

Many a person has sworn that, "Once I get X, I'll never ask for more from life." But that's not how human nature works, as the following case histories show.

"I have nothing to be unhappy about but, still, I am unhappy."

Cynthia, 31, was the envy of all her friends. After struggling for 10 years in the city, she had established a successful merchandising career and had her own aparment AND had met the sort of man every single woman dreams of meeting. Tall, good-looking and successful, Paul, 41, was madly in love with Cynthia and wanted nothing more than to have her share his homes, his boats, his children and his love. He was affectionate and adoring and appreciative of everything she did—and he said so: Cynthia "looked beautiful," her cooking was "perfection," "she was wonderful." In his eyes, she could do no wrong. On their wedding day, Cynthia could not believe her good luck. Yet, six months later, she is miserable. Why? Everything Paul had promised had come true: She did share his life with him—and that was the problem—it was HIS life, full of HIS homes, HIS boats, HIS children, HIS success. She felt like one of HIS possessions and as though she no longer had any control over her life. It was hard for Cynthia to say so—particularly since everyone was always saying what a good life she had with Paul—but all was not ideal in this idyll she was living. Indeed, she did have "a good life" except, she said, she had to live it in response to his whims and needs. And she felt deprived of the attention Paul had showered on her in their courtship. Oh, he still was affectionate, but now that they were ensconced in their marriage, he had reverted to his workaholic pattern—one that Cynthia had been unaware of. Cynthia told Paul he should work less and spend more time with her. But her message was not well-received. Aside from underscoring the fact that he enjoyed his work a great deal, Paul also told Cynthia not to forget that her "good life" would soon deteriorate if he did not work hard at being successful. In addition, he responded to her complaint by becoming critical of her personal habits: She left her clothes strewn about the bathroom, left the cap off the toothpaste, the soap in the sink. He complained that she wasn't "nice" enough to or "concerned" enough about his children when they visited.

In the course of counseling, Cynthia came to realize that she actually did have "something" to be unhappy about, however rosy the surface of her life appeared to be.

Once she accepted this and saw the root of her problem, Cynthia set about doing something to control *her* role in it. The root of what troubled Cynthia was that everything in this life of "theirs" belonged to Paul. Worse, she ACTED as though everything (including herself) was HIS. Cynthia was behaving not like a wife or partner to Paul, but like a house guest, or like his live-in girl-friend.

As is true of many men with newly acquired wealth, Paul had to feel that Cynthia was "paying her way" and not merely "along for the ride" in this marriage. In effect, he wanted her to earn her

132

keep by keeping his houses clean and running smoothly—there'd be no housekeepers for his homes, so long as he had a wife to run them. He even insisted she do windows. Paul made it very clear how he saw her role—Cynthia was not *imagining* her way into a Cinderella casting that doomed her forever to life with the wrong prince. Finally, she asserted herself. This was no longer to be HIS marriage, but their marriage, she told Paul. And she insisted on sharing property ownership and upon having legal documents drawn up to that effect. Surprisingly, he agreed that their marriage should be THEIR marriage and he complied readily. Cynthia said, too, that she appreciated the value of his work and that he must appreciate the value of hers as well—and she retuned to merchandising, which gave her feelings of pride and independence and money of her own. Her third ultimatum—also readily acceded to by Paul—was that, within two years, they would have a child—THEIR child.

Cynthia was again engaged in the *process* of living a happy life and in continuing on her *journey*, realizing that to succeed as a responsible and enriched being, she must view each achievement as yet another beginning—never as an ending or as an end in and of itself.

"I got what I aimed for, but now I'm not happy—and I don't know what to do."

After 11 years of marriage—and happiness— Susan has come to realize that she is unhappy and

133

says she doesn't know what to do about it. At 23, she thought she had achieved all the goals that would ever matter in her life and, for several years, she enjoyed all of her achievements thoroughly. She and Don had met in college and had fallen totally in love. Immediately after graduation, they married and it was obvious each cherished and felt cherished by the other. But as the years passed, their contentment diminished and gave way to a vague discontent—with their lives and with one another. At 33, she talks about having children and thinks about it, but is afraid to because she finds her marriage so unrewarding. She has not developed a career, has a very limited circle of friends and family and has an extremely limited income. Susan feels uneasy in social situations and finds it difficult to blend in with new people. She knows she would feel better if she had a job but is afraid Don would object. Troubled as she is about her marriage, she loves her husband and doesn't want to threaten her relationship with Don further.

Obviously, working, meeting more people, facing new challenges and becoming involved with interesting situations would make life—and Susan—far more interesting to herself and to Don. Despite her initial statement to the contrary, she knows this.

When we say we don't know why we're unhappy, generally what we really mean is that we're afraid to face the problem—and/or the solution. However, if problems aren't faced, if changes aren't made, life becomes stagnant. There can be no excitement without aim or purpose. Growth cannot occur without change.

Although like Susan and (many people) you may fear change, rest assured that making changes in your life does not necessarily require you to change things that are important to you.

Susan actually may help her relationship with her husband—and may even help him, too—by actively creating a life that is more vital and interesting, rather than just *accepting* the one she has. The fear of loss is not always well-founded and certainly, maintaining stagnation will not insure against loss. Sometimes, it can even make loss inevitable.

Susan's dreams came true and for a decade they served her well. But we do not survive in a vacuum and neither do our dreams. When Susan awoke to the need for change, she gave up old ways for new ones so that what she most cherished would thrive.

"I'm in a rut and I don't know how to get out of it."

Jack is bored. He feels he is in a rut and says he doesn't know how to get out of it. Like Susan, his professed "not knowing" is really an attempt to maintain the status quo—his afraid to change.

He goes to work every day, leaving at 7 a.m., and he returns home at 7 p.m. every night, has dinner with Jean, his wife of nearly five years, then sits and watches TV while she spends her evenings working on reports for her job as a management consultant. Jack feels lonely and neglected and is very angry at Jean's preoccupation with her job. He makes more than enough money, he says— she doesn't *have* to work. But Jean insists on working. She says she needs the feelings of

135

independence and self-esteem she derives from her career. Things were fine when they both worked for the same company and shared the commute and the long working hours. However, almost a year ago, when he accepted a new job—and a promotion to a senior management position at another corporation—they began taking separate ways to work and their lives began taking separate paths. Jack complains that he is in a rut of isolation. He says doing things alone is the pits; he wants to do more with his life, preferably with his wife.

There are many working couples and Jack's problem is a common one today. As women move into more demanding positions, they often have work that takes them away from their families or from their spouses. Many young men, like Jack, understand the obligations of equality, and consider themselves "liberal-minded" and accepting of these obligations, but they are traditionalists at heart and truly want their wives available to them upon demand, performing in the traditional role.

For this period of time, Jean is working hard to earn a promotion. Though Jack says she is being rigid about pursuing her career goals, she points out that he always has been in "a rut" as far as activities go, and never took the initiative to pursue hobbies or interests without her, on his own. He didn't like hearing it, but Jack faced this observation of Jean's and admitted it was true. Shortly after acknowledging the truth of this, he made contact with a friend whose carpentry shop is now at his disposal for his wood-working hobby. Jack also rejoined his health club and made it a point to meet regularly with his political club cronies.

Jack married the kind of woman he thought he always wanted—with a career of her own, who would not be dependent on him. But he hadn't counted on his own dependency and deep-rooted expectation that his wife would be the kind of girl who'd married dear old Dad.

"I never thought my life would turn out like this."

Steve, the father of two, is 45, has been married for 15 years, has a lovely home in the suburbs, and finds himself haunting the old neighborhood of his bachelor days.

"I didn't get married till I was 30 and I thought, at the time, that I knew what I wanted. Now, 15 years later, I can't believe I commute two and one-half hours a day to and from my house in the sticks—and that I have to spend my free time on the weekends taking care of it! I loved my bachelor apartment in the city and like to stroll around near it sometimes before heading home.

"I moved to the suburbs so that my wife and children could live in a safe and pleasant environment but I feel alive only in the city and keep thinking of ways to move back. "My wife is nice, but not exciting—just like my children. In fact, that describes my life in the burbs—nice, but not exciting. Fortunately, my public relations job is interesting and sometimes even exciting, and that keeps me going."

137

Steve is someone who knew what he wanted but who subverted his goals to do "the right thing"—give his family a nice home. But he is so unhappy that he is making them unhappy, though they don't understand what the problem is. Everyone is so afraid of finding out what the matter might be that they're studiously avoiding any discussion of it—and becoming more and more uneasy.

There is no easy solution to this problem. Steve's wife and children have always liked the life he has provided for them and Steve, though he regrets ever having moved out of town, feels he cannot ask his family to uproot itself and return to the city. So he suffers in silence. There are alternatives to such behavior. Steve and his wife might choose to get the problem out in the open and discuss it between themselves. After they have begun to understand it as husband and wife, and have a few ideas on how to handle it that are mutually satisfying, they might then discuss it with their children. Both boys—12 and 14—are old enough to understand the situation and might even have suggestions to offer. Certainly, they will all be relieved to learn that their father is not unhappy because of something they did or failed to do and will welcome the opportunity to function as a family—something Steve's silent solo suffering has not allowed them to do.

"I am making changes I want to make—even though I have to hurt others to do so."

Bob and Ann were high school sweethearts who married the June they graduated. She worked while he completed both college and law school

138

and was glad to do it; proud of his academic accomplishments. Today, 23 years later, he has a well-established law practice and she has established a comfortable home for Bob and their teen-agers, a boy and a girl. Ann has been supportive of Bob throughout the years and instrumental in building his career through her advice and through her graciousness as a hostess both to the clients he entertained over the years, and to his colleagues. Now that he is comfortable financially, confident about his professional abilities and reasonably sure that his family is on sound footing, Bob could be congratulating himself in accomplishing his teen-aged goals. Instead, he is obsessed with unrealized goals— to have all the good times he missed, to sow all the wild oats he never had time to sow, to sleep with all the cheerleaders he never got a chance to know. Bob has been a hard-working man all his life. Now he wants the fun and partying he missed as he earnestly climbed his way up the career ladder. He wants to party *as a single person*, he told Ann—and, he added repeatedly, he wants to experience other women—many other women. He says—quite sincerely—that he loves his wife and children and does not want to give up family life. But he hastens to say that he can't and won't live the rest of his life having achieved the first half of his goals without trying to achieve the second half. For years he had suppressed his boyish fantasies of a free-wheeling bachelor's sex life. With the evolution of more liberal attitudes toward sex over the years, the fantasies would not be suppressed but grew stronger until he could think of little else. He wants to make a drastic change in his life style so he can finally get the cheerleader he always wanted—perhaps the entire cheerleading squad. Once this is out of his system, he says, he would like to be able to come home again.

Probably in two years, Bob will be looking for someone like his wife—a companion who is comfortably settled and comfortable to be settled with—rather than for someone to party with. Meanwhile, he insists that he must do this. Ann was stunned and hurt and emotionally devastated at the news but is now quietly making plans to make the change as non-threatening to herself and her children as possible. And she has told him to quietly look for a "swinging singles" residence for himself and then to take all his belongings with him because she will need room to create a new life for herself without him. Ann is furious and says she does not wish him well.

Bob is a man who has not relinquished the fantasies he has held since he was 18 years old. In fact, he has made goals of them. They might have been appropriate for him as a high school senior but they seem not so appropriate for a 41-year-old family man. Nevertheless, they are a driving force in his mind and he will not give them up, will not rest, until he pursues them whatever the cost. He feels it would be best for himself and his family, too, for him to leave and put this demon to rest.

Perhaps if Bob had been less single-minded in the pursuit of his achieved goals, if he and Ann had had more fun mixed into the earnestness of their lives, these fantasies would have faded as many teen-age fantasies do.

All of us tend to get caught up in the particulars of life and to lose sight of the larger picture by concentrating on details. Tending to schedules and commitments, we often lose sight of our purpose. We plunge ahead, urging ourselves onward, but forget to review our destinations.

It sometimes helps to stop the action and assess what we are doing. It may be that we will find ourselves on a track we don't remember choosing and that it is time to switch directions.

Ask yourself: "Am I the engine or the caboose?"
Ask yourself: "Am I caught up on someone else's goals, or am I pursuing my own?"

Any good storekeeper closes shop and takes inventory at least once a year. Taking a psychic inventory is a good idea too—and the oftener, the better. Take your own inventory, by trying these exercises:

1. Think about your teen-age fantasies. How did you dream your life *now* would be when you were *younger?* Do you still have any of the same fantasies? Have any of them come true? Can you distinguish "fantasies" from "goals?" What would you still like to do that you wanted to do then, but haven't "gotten around to" doing? How can you go about accomplishing this goal or fulfilling this fantasy?

141

2. Though we don't like to think of it, sometimes it makes us very aware of our real feelings if we face the fact that we're not going to live forever. Imagine, then, that you have only six months to live—how would you spend your time? Looking at your goals and your life in this way helps you focus on the things most important to you. What are you doing to achieve them? Can you—should you—step up your efforts in this direction?

3. Imagine *in detail* how you would like to be living five years from now. What would you have to do to change your present lifestyle? How would you begin? Start planning accordingly. And leave room for enjoyment—by choosing to enjoy who you are, who you meet and the challenges that lie ahead.

SUMMARY:

Working hard to achieve goals is necessary and commendable and rewarding. But don't expect to rest on your laurels once your goals have been reached. Success really IS a journey, as the Zen philosophers teach. It is not a destination.

Fearing change, many of us hold fast to the bench in the train station and never get on the train—never take the journey. Others board the train but keep their eyes turned toward their departure point, long after it has faded from view, and never notice all the new wonders that pass them by.

Travel lightly—don't hang onto old baggage, don't keep looking homeward (at the past) or staring at a point on a map labeled "Goal" or "Destination." Be aware of where you are NOW and of the riches available to you.

Bon Voyage!

CHAPTER X

YOU'RE READY, YOU'RE SET—SO GO!

"I celebrate myself and sing myself . . ."
—Walt Whitman, "Song of Myself"

Walt Whitman was an avowed atheist, but he had the gist of most religions and practiced it —he loved *himself* and he loved others.

If you believe in a creator or a cosmic power or in the wonder of existence or in simply today, take strength from that belief to celebrate yourself and to live your moments as they occur. No one is exactly like you. You are special and complex and have something special and complex to give to the world in which you live—and, in your own very special way, you can get from it things that no one else can get.

For your own sake—reach out and take it—don't wait for it to fall in your lap. Patrick Denis's character, Auntie Mame, said "Life's a banquet and most poor bastards are starving to death." Give yourself the right to go to the banquet—simply being alive means you've been invited.

Throughout this book, we've urged you to take stock, make plans, choose alternatives to give yourself the ways and means to enjoy life more, to give yourself the go-ahead to be the happy person you have the right to be. We've advocated making lists, making plans, commitments to yourself—to take a chance, make an effort, risk a failure. Essentially—we are urging you to set yourself free from old habits, old reactions and to trade in reactions for actions.

In the end, we are what we *do*.

What happens to us may be out of our control at times, but what we *do* with what occurs in our lives is what matters, is what rings up the total of our lives. Helen Keller had every excuse in the world to sit back and bemoan her fate—who could have blamed her? But she filled her dark and silent world with beauty. She defied the odds to communicate with the world and to share the wonders she had been able to extract from living, from being all she *could* be.

All our battles are heroic. Some get the spotlight and applause from the world or from friends but the most important battles are quiet, unsung and noticed only by a few, if any. Our battles, largely, are fought alone.

Leaving home, looking for a new job, going back to school after years away, committing yourself to loving and trusting another, going into debt to accomplish a goal, announcing to the world that you are once again going to quit smoking—and daring to be proud of yourself for trying again, rather than ashamed of yourself for having failed previously—all of these are victories.

Failures are victories. They are like stamps on your passport indicating your travels, indicating your *efforts*, indicating your *actions*. A passport is not a report card. Report cards are given out at the end of your journey—and *you* do the grading. "Show me a

145

person who makes no mistakes and I'll show you a person who makes no efforts," goes an old saying.

If you stop playing the rating game, if you stop giving yourself judgmental marks, and do things for the reward and satisfaction of trying, you'll be a happy person.

In the last chapter, we wished you *bon voyage*. We are urging you to validate your own passport, grant yourself 1st-class passenger status and embark on the greatest journey ever taken. It starts not by going round the world, however, but in the deep, dark, interior regions of yourself which have been generally uncharted and unexplored and, as a result, feared. (People generally fear the unknown, why should you be an exception?)

But why should you *continue* to live in fear? Chart the unknown shores of yourself. Cherish your discoveries. Accept yourself. Be proud of your accomplishments and your failures. Make plans for the future and for the day—but don't become a slave to your plans; feel free to change them. The whole point of taking charge of yourself and your life is to make yourself comfortable, as a private person, as a relative, a spouse, a lover, a friend, an employee or employer, as a citizen, as a neighbor, as a student, a hobbyist, a dreamer and a doer. There are many facets of you and sometimes they require different things from life.

Previously, we spoke of letting go of old things to make room for new ones. Try to give up old definitions of yourself—the ones you've gotten from others, the ones embroidered with words like "should" and "ought" and trade them in for new ones, that come from new discoveries about yourself . . . yourself and your new needs. And, for good measure, get rid of old re-

grets, you know the ones—they start with "if only"—
and toss out the usual worries about new situations
(generally, they begin with "what if").

Some of us *like* to be "defined" by others—it saves
us the trouble of doing it ourselves. But those who
have tried self-definition wouldn't rate the adventure
of it all under any circumstances. Living up to the
definitions and expectations others have for us is
unrewarding at best. It puts us in the position of a
family pet—we perform our obligations, run through
our tricks, for a much needed pat from the master and
his household. Much better to be the master than the
pet. Much better to give ourselves pats when we need
them, to take responsibility for our own well-being.

The trouble with most definitions is that they don't
change. But life changes. Your needs change. And if
you don't make changes to accommodate these
conditions, you'll become very uncomfortable. You
won't be a happy person.

How do you feel, right now, about yourself as a
private individual (as opposed, say, to yourself as a
mate or a parent or an employee)? Feelings tell us
what's good and what's in need of changing in our
lives. And how we feel and what we need are our best
definitions of who we are. If we feel uncomfortable
about how we have reacted to another person, it is
likely that another approach will make us and the
other feel better. If we feel regret at having gone off
our diet, we need to reassure ourselves—lovingly—
that we deserve to succeed at this goal and that we
owe it to ourselves to have the pleasure of trying
again. Self-improvement does not require self-flagel-
lation. It requires self-love. If you give yourself the
very best of treatment, you will treat others the same

147

way—with love. And, probably, they will respond in kind.

When is the last time you watched an infant learn to walk? Isn't it too bad we can't talk at that age—it would be fascinating to hear our thoughts. We totter and fall and get hurt and cry and get up and do it all again and again. The pain just can't outweigh the joy of being able to move about on our own. Once we have tasted the promise of this freedom a step at a time—we *will* have it.

Too few of us have the courage of babies.

Perhaps, observing the walkers of the world from our cribs and playpens makes us realize that walking is something we are meant to do. Perhaps a genetic code demands that we walk. But no one rises from crib or playpen and suddenly starts jogging. Everything gets done a step at a time. We crawl before we walk. And we fall a lot, too. If we'd viewed the falls as failures, we'd never have survived.

There are steps to take that help us "get someplace" in this life. One is to explore who we are, what we have, what we give, what we need, where we are and where we'd like to be. Once we have a clear picture of what IS and what CAN BE, once we have determined what WE WANT, we can set about getting it.

VISUALIZING what we want is a tool worth using. A good time to do this is before going to sleep at night and before rising in the morning. Think clearly of the change you want to effect and of how your life in the coming day will be as you work to achieve that change. Perhaps it involves being calm in the presence of someone with whom you usually feel uncomfortable. Imagine meeting that person. Imagine what you will say to one another, and how, this time, when your discomfort begins, you will tell yourself comforting things. And you will reassure yourself of your worth, of the fact that things will go well with you at this moment. Encourage the other person to think comfortable thoughts, in your imagined encounter, by saying something positive about the issue at hand or something general about your surroundings. Imagine yourself feeling comfortable and calm even in the face of a rebuff from this person. And imagine yourself afterwards, proud of your ability to have done so well. Perhaps, instead of a grumpy person, you must face a new situation—meet new people, despite your shyness, or endure a job interview, despite great nervousness. Imagine yourself bearding the lion in its den—and doing a creditable job of it. Each time you visualize, improve upon your performance. And, when the time comes, you will make it happen.

If you feel you do not accomplish enough during the day, visualize all that you want to get done and how you will go about it before you fall asleep, and again before you get up. By the time you start your day, you will have charted your course to sail through it as smoothly as possible. And be flexible—do remember that you are charting your course to make life run smoothly, to make it easier to get from one point to another—not to give yourself something else to fret about. If you hit a snag, adjust. When you visualize yourself in action, make allowances for exceptions to the plan. Congratulate yourself for your ability to improvize when you move from visualization to *actualization* (to actually doing it). Visualizing affirms your belief in your ability to realize a goal, to affect a change. It is a process that can strengthen your faith in yourself and your goals.

We have suggested that you imagine a dire situation—that you have just learned your life will end in six month's time. How would you react?

Would you curl up and wait for the end to come?

Would you make plans to put your financial and ethical house in order, clearing your ledgers of debts, both emotional and fiscal?

Would you abandon your relationships and obligations and run off to see the world?

Would you go hot-air ballooning with your spouse, the kids, Aunt Hattie and the cat?

List all your goals—all the things you'd like to do in your lifetime. Then list all your negatives—your fears, your resentments, your angers, your jealousies. List all your fantasies: Things I'd Like to Do. List all your excuses: Reasons Why I Can't do Them. (They'll likely include: Lack of money; lack of time; I'm too old; I'm too young; I have too many responsibilities; People (my wife/husband/parents/boss/neighbors/commitments) won't allow it; I lack the training; I live in the wrong town/country/universe.)

Now, assuming you actually have done some traveling into the Interior of You and have become a bit familiar with some formerly unexplored continents of heart, mind, soul and body, kindly and realistically and reassuringly start eliminating your excuses.

There are no sure things in life, no right answers, no one way to happiness, no rainbow's end. And that's great—there is no one rainbow but many rainbows and if you missed one or two along the way, you'll find others—when you are ready—provided you keep moving.

There are no endings in this life, happy or otherwise. There are only beginnings. One door closes, another opens. Each goal achieved grants its reward—and it's new challenges. People like to say that there are only two sure things in this world—death and taxes. Well, there are lots of people who can evade their taxes, at least for a while, but nobody evades death. In fact, we all spend our lifetimes in preparation for death. And you know what—that's probably not an ending either.

But while we're here, let's get to know and enjoy as much as we can, starting with ourselves. Be sure to say hello to the most central character you'll ever meet—you—before you have to say goodbye.

SUMMARY:

Hello, voyager. Welcome to the world of you. May your journey be a rich and happy one.